PLANTS AND
HUMAN ECONOMICS

LONDON
Cambridge University Press
FETTER LANE

NEW YORK · TORONTO
BOMBAY · CALCUTTA · MADRAS
Macmillan

TOKYO
Maruzen Company Ltd

PLANTS AND
HUMAN ECONOMICS

by

RONALD GOOD, M.A. (Cantab.)

Head of the Department of Botany
University College, Hull

WITH 8 MAPS

CAMBRIDGE
AT THE UNIVERSITY PRESS
1933

PRINTED IN GREAT BRITAIN

TO

P. G. G.

CONTENTS

MAPS

Maps 1–6. Maps of the Continents showing the distribution of the cultivation of the more important plant crops. Natural sources of commercial plant products are also shown.

In the case of the most important products the maps are, as far as possible for their size, complete, but in the case of drugs, spices, oil-seeds, tropical fruits and miscellaneous commodities it has been possible to include only some of the more outstanding or interesting items. As regards fruits, the word FRUIT is used to cover the Prunus and Pyrus fruits generally since a locality usually produces more than one kind. The word CITRUS also is used to cover all the members of that genus. Where more than one product is obtained from a plant the name of the plant is given, as for instance FLAX, and the actual product for which it is grown locally is not shown.

Hawaii and Polynesia are not shown on the maps. Their products are much those of other places in similar latitudes.

It must be remembered that this is a map,
somewhat simplified, of natural vegetation as it
is, or would be, unaffected by the influence of
man. Thus Great Britain is shown as forest and
Egypt as desert, but both are in fact now densely
cultivated and their original condition has been
much modified.

Under the heading of desert are included not
only the warm deserts like the Sahara but also the
polar and alpine treeless zones. It is impossible
in so small a map to show all the minor isolated
patches of the last named.

Much of the area shown as hard-wood forest
should, on a larger scale, be shown as savannah or
park land, a type of vegetation characterised by
scattered trees with more or less continuous grass
between them. They are shown here as forest because, for the most part, the presence of the trees
prevents them from being exploited in the same
way as the pure grasslands.

The purpose of this map is principally to indicate the position of the major forest regions of
the world whence comes the supply of commercial
timbers. The insertion of the tropic lines serves to
discriminate to some extent between temperate
and tropical timber sources.

PREFACE

Education, like every other phase of human progress, advances by a gradual process of evolution. At present it is in the "examination" stage, and the opinion is widely held that future generations who shall be able, by the passage of time, to review the present in something like a true perspective will deplore this period. Be this as it may, the examination system is with us and from it we cannot as yet escape. Meanwhile we must exploit its good points and do what we can to remedy its defects.

This little book is a small attempt to do something in the latter way for a particular subject—botany. It is remarkable that the aspect of botany most intimately concerning human affairs and activities, economic botany, is the aspect least taught. Whether the examination system is to be blamed for this or not is uncertain, because the result is as likely to be cause as effect, but the fact remains that in the educational circumstances of to-day there is often a tendency for botany to be regarded merely as a constituent of certain scholastic fences which have to be surmounted before what is popularly supposed to be open country is reached. The student's view of the science tends to be bounded by a syllabus, and of its implications he learns little.

My object has therefore been to combine in small compass and, it is hoped, in reasonable and readable fashion, not only the botanical facts but also, and frequently more important, the historical and economic facts required to give to those who begin the scientific study of botany an adequate humanistic background of reality to their subject. I have tried to give them the evidence that the science of plants is something more than a mere mental discipline.

Although this book is intended primarily for those in the senior classes of schools and the junior classes of universities,

I have been at some pains to make it also of potential value to those who do not happen to be students of biology, not only by including an elementary account of plant-physiology, but also by making the later chapters as complete as their size permits, so that they can be used to some extent for reference. It may be assumed that they include mention of all but the very uncommon and local plant products. At the same time it has been necessary, in these later chapters, to make use of some botanical terms without stopping to define them.

The preparation of this book has naturally led me to refer to a great many other publications, and to give a complete list of these would be impracticable as well as of doubtful value. Instead there will be found, just before the Appendix, a short list of selected references, chosen for the most part as outstanding examples of their kinds or as works from which still other and more detailed bibliographies can be obtained.

I am much indebted to Dr B. T. Cromwell for reading the more physiological parts of the manuscript and to those others of my colleagues who have been good enough to give me their opinions on particular points of difficulty.

RONALD GOOD

Hull
5 March 1933

Chapter I

INTRODUCTORY

Swift's great satire, *Gulliver's Travels*, provides us with a quotation which forms an excellent opening for a book on Economic Botany.

Gulliver is describing some of the political features of his country to the King of Brobdingnag. His Majesty becomes more and more scornful of them and concludes the interview by giving his opinion "that whoever could make two ears of corn, or two blades of grass, to grow upon a spot of ground where only one grew before, would deserve better of Mankind, and do more essential service to his Country, than the whole race of Politicians put together". Whether this sweeping condemnation of political methods, for that was its intention, was justified or not is a matter of opinion which does not concern us here. The importance of the statement lies rather in the vivid way in which it brings to mind and emphasises the fundamental relation between human welfare and the plant world. We have advanced far since the early part of the eighteenth century, when Swift was writing, but subsequent events have done little or nothing to alter the opinion then expressed, although they have perhaps caused it to become a little less obvious. Our debt towards the plant world and our reliance upon it for the essentials of our existence still remains of first importance to the human race. Little apology is therefore needed for this small book, which tries to set forth as completely as it may, within its small compass, the facts which form the basis of the opinions expressed so long ago by the ruler of Brobdingnag.

The most fundamental fact about the human race and its material well-being, is that, biologically at any rate, man is an animal and is in many respects no different from the other members of the great class of the mammals. It is true that man has, by the development of reason and intellect, risen to a position of dominance over other living things, but the high level of culture and civilisation which he has attained has in no way sufficed to change the totally animal nature of his life-processes. Only in the exercise of his intelligence is he really superior, and even here his superiority is often more apparent than real.

The most important result of this relationship is that, like other animals, man is dependent on his environment, that is to say the earth and the atmosphere, for all his material necessities. Man's superior culture has increased rather than lowered his dependence in this respect because it has so largely added to his wants. The only requirements of an ordinary animal are sufficient food, often of the most simple and monotonous kind, and, in most cases, some degree of shelter. Man's requirements are the same, but only in the lowest races are they at all comparable in simplicity. In all the higher human races they are much more complex. Diets are more varied, luxuries attain the status of necessities, clothing is essential, and far more is required to give the desired shelter and protection.

Yet all these things must be produced from the environment, that is to say, they must be obtained by the exploitation of natural resources. The part that the plant world plays in supplying them is our subject here.

The first requirement of every living thing is an adequate supply of suitable food, in the absence of which starvation will result. But man in a state of civilisation needs, besides this, a vast number of other commodities, many of them raw materials for conversion into useful articles, and this latter need becomes augmented with increased culture. Therefore we can regard the various plant products which we shall later describe as falling into two classes, food materials and other commodities, and it is convenient to consider them in this way and in this order.

This clearly leads us to the subject of trade, which is perhaps the most characteristic activity of the human race. Among wild animals uncontrolled competition for the more or less limited food available maintains a just balance between demand and supply, so that no region normally contains a greater animal population than it can support by its own food production. In man, however, civilisation has tended gradually to remove the restrictive powers of competition or at least to modify them considerably so that they become relatively ineffective. As a result there is commonly seen in the human race a condition of affairs rarely, and then only temporarily, seen in other animals —the occupation of a region by a population far in excess of the maximum possible production. Most of the highly civilised countries of the world are in this state at the present time and contain more people than they can reasonably supply with necessities from within their own borders. Nevertheless these necessities must be forthcoming if the people are to survive. This can be secured in one way only, by obtaining supplies from other countries which can spare them. What cannot be produced must be bought or bartered, that is, obtained by trade. The degree to which countries are dependent on trade, and especially on mutual trade, varies almost directly with the degree of civilisation they show. In very primitive communities the needs of the individual are so simple that they can generally be met by the individual's own unaided efforts, so that he is more or less self-supporting and under little or no obligation to his fellow-men. But for various reasons the more highly organised and civilised a society becomes the less this simple state of affairs is possible and the greater becomes the division of labour. The production of particular commodities becomes confined to particular groups of the population, and the remainder are dependent for their share of the commodity on this group. Hence the more complicated a human society is, the less and less true it is that the consumer is also the producer, or *vice versa*, and thus there develops trade, which is the exchange of one commodity for another.

In its simplest condition trade is merely barter, that is to say, the exchange of one kind of article for an approximately equal amount or value of another. Barter is adequate as a trade method so long as all members of a population produce at least some amount of a useful commodity, but most civilisations have long passed this stage. When this happens it becomes necessary to have some common medium of exchange which can be earned by any member of the community even if he is not a direct producer of commercial material, and with which he can buy what he wants. This medium of exchange is, of course, money.

Except in the least civilised countries, where by hunting or agriculture each head of a family or each individual can obtain directly by his own efforts enough support for himself and his dependents, trade, either domestic or international, must be the basis of the welfare of the population. In some countries, where the population is small and the standard of living and general level of requirement is low, trade is almost entirely a domestic affair. The needs of the people can be met from within their own boundaries and their relationship with other countries is small. In countries where the population, or rather the density of population, is high, the reverse is the case and the great bulk of trade is international, because the country has to rely on others for the greater part of its necessities.

That man is no exception to the invariable rule that life can only be maintained when food supplies are adequate, is shown by the comparatively frequent occurrence of famine in different parts of the world. Famine conditions appear when, for one or more of many reasons, the available food becomes insufficient for the numbers that have to share it. The two ultimate causes of famine are the failure of crops and the bad distribution of food. Among the most common contributory causes to one or both of these are: dry seasons causing less than normal crop yield; frosts unusually late in spring or early in autumn; seasons in which, through lack of sunshine, proper ripening does not take place; the ravages of plant diseases or plant pests, like locusts; the spoiling of harvests after gathering and before they can be distributed. Many other factors, especially those, which like war, disturb normal economic conditions, and those which concern the lack of transport facilities, affect the distribution of food.

In past centuries famines were liable to occur almost anywhere but, with the lessening of geographical isolation and the development of communications and trade routes, the danger of famine has now been practically diverted from highly civilised countries. To-day it occurs chiefly in the more remote parts of the world where a backward population depends almost entirely upon one staple food. Such conditions obtain especially in India and China and, in those countries, famines of a more or less serious character recur at frequent intervals. It has been said that there are over one million deaths from famine and its attendant diseases in India every year. The natives live almost exclusively on grain grown in the country, where the transport facilities are none too good and, in seasons of deficient harvests, want is soon felt. Extensive relief measures have to be undertaken and even these are usually not enough to prevent widespread distress. China, too, has suffered many devastating famines, as during the Taiping rebellion in the middle of last century, as well as on many subsequent occasions, and it is indeed probably true to say that in some part of that huge country food shortage is, to some extent, always present.

Even in highly civilised countries the danger of famine is not altogether absent. Less than a century ago the potato crops in Ireland, which formed the bulk of the food supplies of the country, were suddenly and irretrievably damaged by a plant disease. Terrible distress resulted despite all the efforts to avert it and the "Hunger" left a permanent impress on the subsequent history of the country. From it dates the gradual depopulation of Ireland in the latter half of the nineteenth century. An accident of disease brought a calamity which all existing knowledge was powerless to prevent and which played the major part in the ultimate reduction of the population to half its previous figure.

But accident is not the only danger. By far the commonest causes of famines are wars resulting from the deliberate actions of human beings, wars which, by interfering with communications and with the peaceful pursuit of agriculture, inevitably tend to cause food shortage. Those who experienced the privations in this country during the latter years of the Great War need no reminder of this, and it is well to remember that while our position was bad that of the enemy countries was far worse. Then, as so often previously, blockade proved itself more potent than the armies in the field. Russia, particularly, suffered terribly in the years immediately following the revolution of 1917.

The foregoing paragraphs are sufficient to give a very elementary explanation of the nature and causes of commerce and to prepare us for a more detailed investigation of the plant products of commerce, but before we leave this introductory chapter there are one or two matters of more general botanical importance which must be mentioned. The first is an outline of the contents of the plant kingdom, and the second is the question of plant names.

The plant kingdom as a whole is divided into two great parts, one containing those plants which reproduce by seeds, Phanerogamia, and the other those plants reproducing by less obvious means, Cryptogamia.

The Phanerogamia contains, in turn, two classes of plants: Flowering Plants (Angiosperms) and Conifers (Gymnosperms).

The Cryptogamia contains five main classes besides several other minor ones which can be neglected here. These five important classes are: Ferns and their allies (Pteridophytes); Mosses and Liverworts (Bryophytes); Algae; Fungi; Bacteria.

There are thus seven main classes with which we shall be directly concerned. In the sea the members of the Algae are practically the only class represented, but on land, throughout the whole world, the great bulk of the plant population is composed of Flowering Plants or Angiosperms. It is, therefore, not surprising to find that it is this group of plants which above all others supplies commercial plants. So much so is this the case that it is convenient to consider all the economic plants which belong to other classes in a separate chapter towards the end of the book. Elsewhere, with one exception which will be explained in due course, we shall be concerned only with Angiosperms.

The question of plant names requires rather more explanation. We are all familiar with people whose botany consists merely of strings of Latin names which often are easily acquired and sound impressive, but which too frequently conceal a very superficial knowledge. This and other difficulties which need not be mentioned have given to botanical nomenclature, as the study of plant names is called, a somewhat undesirable reputation. This is unfortunate, because an understanding of the use and proper employment of Latin names is, as we shall see, essential. In the first place it is necessary to employ Latin for the purpose of names simply as an international language, and one which can be translated into the same terms whatever the native language of the user may be. It is simply a matter of using labels which will be beyond the limitations of national speech. It may, however, be urged that if we are English people reading a book in English written primarily for English people, why need we bother about other people—let them do the same thing for their own language. The answer to this is twofold. In arguing in this way we are simply being narrow-minded. Science has no national boundaries, and if we have knowledge to impart we should make it as widely available as possible. This reply alone is sufficient, but there is another aspect as well. Latin names are, for reasons which will be explained, *official* names, and no two plants bear the same one: English names are far from official, a particular name in one part of the country may be unknown somewhere else, and one plant may be called a dozen different things. Moreover there are no accurate descriptions of the plants to which English names are applied, and it commonly happens either that one plant has several names or that several plants are called by the

same name, so that there is no way of distinguishing between
them.

However, the value of Latin names can be best illustrated by
explaining how they are used and applied. The basal unit of
plant classification is the species, and every species possesses,
according to a code of internationally agreed rules, two Latin
names, given to it after it has been described in detail by a com-
petent botanist, and which cannot be altered arbitrarily by
subsequent investigators. The two names correspond closely
to the Christian names and surnames of human beings and
have much the same value. The first name is the generic name,
as it is called, and tells us within narrow limits the kind of plant
we are dealing with. This is, as it were, the surname. The
second or specific name is a kind of Christian name which tells
exactly which one of this kind of plant we are talking about.
For instance *Bellis perennis* is the name of the common daisy.
In other parts of the world there are other species of daisy.
These all have the same generic name *Bellis* but each has a
different specific name, so that there are as many specific names
as there are species. In exactly the same way such a name as
John Smith tells us not only that the individual concerned is
one of a group of related individuals, the Smiths, but also, exactly which of the Smiths he is. Hence the only real difference
between plant names and human names is that, in the former,
the generic or surname comes first, and in the latter it usually
comes last. To take our illustration further we may say that
English plant names are more like nicknames than anything
else. They are in short not legal appellations. The system of
giving each species two Latin names was instituted by the
Swedish biologist Linnaeus in the eighteenth century, and that
great man spent most of his life describing and naming plants
and animals.

Anyone interested in botany should understand something
of scientific plant names, but it is especially necessary for the
study of economic botany because it is there particularly
desirable to distinguish between plants which may be super-

ficially alike but very different in their commercial value. No better example of this can be given than that of some of the numerous plant species which provide timber of commercial value. The case of mahogany is interesting. Mahogany is one of the most valuable of all woods. It comes from a plant species, called scientifically, *Swietenia Mahagoni*, which grows in Tropical America. But quite a number of timbers are called by very similar English names such as African mahogany, Indian mahogany, Australian mahogany, mountain mahogany and so on, and if we accepted these names at their face value we should be justified in supposing that these timbers were all mahogany. The Latin names, however, tell us this is not so. They show that the species from which they come are all quite distinct from one another and not closely related to the plant *Swietenia Mahagoni*, and that their timbers are therefore not true mahogany although they may, and generally do, resemble that wood more or less closely in certain properties. Their English names are misleading and it is not until the Latin names are used that we can be certain of the kind of wood with which we are dealing. Let us take one more example. Oak is a very important timber used, amongst other ways, for parquet floorings. It is rather expensive for the purpose however and there is frequently employed in its place a timber called Australian oak. In point of fact this is the wood of a species of *Eucalyptus* and not at all the same thing as real oak although it may be a useful substitute for it, but the English name alone would not indicate the difference between them.

It must not be supposed that this use of English names is in any way intentionally misleading. They are used generally because they convey roughly the sort of wood, the purpose for which it may be used, and the kinds for which it may be substituted. Often enough the substitute is as good as the real article, indeed even better, or more easily obtainable, but occasionally this is not so and the consequences may be serious. The remedy of course is the use of fixed and invariable Latin names.

Another reason why Latin names are not more often used is that they are often clumsy, perhaps difficult to pronounce, and hardly ever sentimental. As a matter of fact they very often tell us a great deal more about the plant than the English name and help us greatly to understand correctly what it is. Let us take a final example to illustrate this. The English and Latin names of five fairly commonly planted shrubs are respectively: common or cherry laurel (*Prunus Laurocerasus*); spotted laurel (*Aucuba japonica*); bay (*Laurus nobilis*); Portuguese laurel (*Prunus lusitanica*); spurge laurel (*Daphne Laureola*). The English names suggest they are all members of one plant group, but the Latin names show that this is far from being the case: only two of them are nearly related. Neither do the English names tell us which is to be regarded as the "true" laurel, that is to say the Laurel of Triumph of the Ancients. But the Latin names give us the necessary clue and we see from them quite clearly that it is the plant known as *Laurus nobilis*, the familiar bay. The name *Laurus* is simply the Latin for "laurel" and the specified name *nobilis* is most suitable. With this information we need no longer picture the victors of old crowned with a wreath of that singularly undistinguished plant, the common cherry laurel. It follows, too, that its use for commemorative purposes is quite inappropriate.

Latin names of plants are often followed by an abbreviated surname. This is a shortened form of the name of the person who first gave the plant its name. The use of the abbreviation is a requirement of nomenclature designed to make doubly sure that no mistaken identities occur. It is not necessary to go to this length here and the authorities' names are not given. Also in order to avoid wearisome repetition the scientific names are given once only, when the plant concerned is first mentioned and it is afterwards referred to by its English name, which in most cases is considerably shorter. For the same reason the names of the families to which the different species mentioned belong are not given in the text but in a special appendix at the end which contains a list of all species mentioned, arranged in systematic order. The abbreviation "sp." means that the species is unidentified or unnamed; "spp." means that more than one species is involved or used. The use of capitals for certain specific names is not a vagary of the type-setter but accords with one of the rules of nomenclature.

Chapter II

THE NATURE AND SOURCES OF FOOD

In the preceding chapter it was explained that the commodities obtained from plants are of two kinds, food-stuffs and those that may, for convenience, be called raw industrial materials. Important as these latter may be they are not essential to the human race in the same sense as food-stuffs are. Given food-stuffs life would be possible, if not, perhaps, pleasant, without the raw industrial materials, but life without food is totally impossible. It is therefore natural to make food materials the first consideration. But the way to an account of food plants must be paved, first, by some discussion on the nature of food and, secondly, by an explanation of why plants are so important in providing it. The former is the subject of this chapter, the latter the subject of the next.

When we think of all the things which go to fill the shelves of the larder and store-cupboard, the statement that the chemistry of food-stuffs is a complicated business will hardly come as a surprise. Anything approaching a detailed study of the subject would, indeed, fill not only the whole of this book but many others too. It is, nevertheless, possible, as long as we confine ourselves to rather general statements, to give a fairly simple outline of the subject.

Chemical compounds, like other things, can be classified according to their kind into a number of classes or groups. If this is done and the different classes are considered from the point of view of their nutritive value, it will be found that the substances which go to make up animal food (we shall discuss the question of plant food later) belong to six classes only. Actually the facts are more remarkable even than this suggests because the part played by at least two of the classes of compounds is relatively small, though none the less important. In short, food is made up almost entirely of substances belonging to three classes of chemical compounds, while representatives of three other classes are included in small quantities.

These six classes are: proteins, carbohydrates, fats, salts, water and vitamins. No other kinds of chemical compounds are of direct nutritive value to the body, although many may be incidentally absorbed and ultimately converted into more useful substances.

Proteins are for the most part very complex chemical compounds, usually composed of at least six elements: carbon, hydrogen, oxygen, nitrogen, sulphur and phosphorus. Some of the simplest proteins have been synthesised, that is to say manufactured, adequately in chemical laboratories, but this is true *only* of the simplest and not of those which are important as food materials. These are to be found solely in the bodies of living organisms and can be obtained only from this source. They are the compounds from which protoplasm itself, the actual living part of the plant or animal body, is built up. Their molecular weights are generally very high.

Carbohydrates are in one way much simpler compounds since they comprise only the elements carbon, hydrogen and oxygen, but their chemistry is often complicated because of their great variety and high molecular weights. The name carbohydrates is given them because the proportion of hydrogen atoms to oxygen atoms in their molecules is always that found in water, namely 2 to 1. Like proteins they occur in nature only in living or freshly killed animal and plant bodies. There are many kinds of carbohydrates, but two, sugars and starches, are especially important as food and a good deal will have to be said about them later.

Fats and oils (the difference between them is only that the former are solid instead of liquid at ordinary temperatures) resemble carbohydrates in so far that their molecules contain the three elements—carbon, hydrogen and oxygen, but the proportions of these and the way in which they are arranged are quite different and give to the resulting compounds very

distinct properties. The fats, like the proteins and carbohydrates, are found only in plant and animal tissues and in
their remains.

These are the three most familiar kinds of food materials,
and human diets, if they are to be satisfactory, must be made
up of them to a very large extent, although they need not be
present in equal amounts. Food requirements vary considerably according to the nature of the individual and depend
also on the kind of work in which he or she is engaged, so that
it is difficult to give anything but average figures. A very
common estimate is that the daily rations of an ordinary adult
doing an ordinary amount of hard work should contain about
four and a half ounces of proteins, about three and three-
quarter ounces of fats and about fifteen ounces (nearly a
pound) of carbohydrates. Most food-stuffs are particularly
rich in one or other of these three classes, but it is rare to find
edibles which contain any considerable mixture of them. As a
result of this most human diets have to be balanced so that the
foods used supplement one another and fulfil all requirements.
There are many familiar instances of food balance in ordinary
diets such as the eating of butter, which is rich in fats, with
bread which is rich in carbohydrates; or the eating of starchy
vegetables with meat, which contains proteins and fats but
lacks carbohydrates. It is very interesting to see how tradition and usage have associated together certain foods in this
way.

The three other kinds of chemical compounds providing
food materials (mineral salts, water and vitamins) play rather
different rôles. Their presence is absolutely essential for life,
but comparatively small quantities of them are normally
sufficient. It also happens that they are usually so distributed
in nature that they become absorbed, incidentally and un-
observed, with the necessary large quantities of proteins,
carbohydrates and fats, so there is no need to seek them out and
consume them specially. This is well seen in the numerous
mineral salts which play a part in nutrition. Only one of them,

sodium chloride (common table salt), is required in such amount that it has to be treated as a separate item of provision; the others are all contained sufficiently in an ordinary balanced diet. It may be mentioned here that many other animals besides ourselves find it necessary to procure more salt than is contained in the rest of their food, and many are accustomed to travel long distances to and from natural deposits of rock salt.

Much of what has been said about salt applies also to water, except that it is much rarer to find a diet which contains within itself enough water, and most animals have to drink fairly copiously in order to make up the deficiency. An adequate supply of water is necessary for the proper functioning of all living bodies, and most of them are composed to a very great degree of that liquid, a fact that has been put rather crudely in the statement that "even an archbishop is 80 per cent. water". An average human body contains about ten gallons. It is, however, true that the more juicy the diet the less extra water needs to be taken. This is why some familiar animals like rabbits are very seldom seen to drink, although neglect to give them water may cause them suffering, especially if their food is relatively dry.

Human beings normally consume, in liquid form, a good deal of water either pure or flavoured, but it is necessary to be cautious in drawing any conclusion from this, because it is certain that if all drinks were as uninteresting to the palate as water the consumption of them would greatly decline. Except in hot weather or after unusual exercise the consumption of liquids is not, in this country, very often occasioned simply by thirst, which is the evidence of physiological need. It is also well known that the human body can, up to a point, be fairly easily disciplined to a lessened water supply. On the other hand, some water is a prime need and must be taken even during periods of fasting from other foods.

The last class of food substances, the vitamins, is made up of compounds so different from any of the others and of such peculiar interest, that it is necessary to say considerably more about them. Vitamins are far less familiar than water or salts, and it may well be asked what they are. Recent researches have made it possible to give something like an adequate answer to this. They are all complex organic substances with large molecules: two at least are alcohols of high molecular weights; one appears to be an acid and another probably contains nitrogen and sulphur. But however interesting these chemical substances may be in composition, it is their functions and values which chiefly concern us.

The story of the vitamins is of very great interest and a very modern one. Their recognition came about in the following way. About twenty years ago, in the course of a series of experiments on animals to determine the value and effect of a number of different diets and food combinations, it was found that sometimes, even when the food given contained proteins, carbohydrates, fats, water and salts in the most approved quantities, healthy growth did not follow. To ensure this it was necessary to add to the diet small amounts of certain other foods which, as far as could be seen in the light of the existing knowledge, did not add anything appreciable to the diet. The actual amounts of these additional foods needed were so small that their direct nutritive value could not be significant. Clearly the explanation, as seems obvious now, was that in these additional food-stuffs there was unintentionally added some substance which, when present, ensured healthy growth, or at any rate prevented the development of unhealthy conditions. To these hypothetical substances the name of "accessory food factors" was first given, but as their importance and nature became clearer this was changed to the more convenient name "vitamins". The existence of the vitamins having been discovered, an enormous amount of research upon them followed, and to-day our knowledge of them is considerable and a whole series of them is recognised. At the same time they are known chiefly from their effects and not from direct investigation because, as has been said, none of them has ever been isolated in any quantity. Because of this ignorance of their exact nature the different vitamins are known by the letters of the alphabet and not by names. Their rôle in human physiology can be best described by considering one or two of the most familiar.

One of the most interesting is vitamin C which, when present in diet, prevents the development of scurvy. In the old days of long sailing-ship voyages sailors were obliged to live for long periods on salted meat and other preserved foods of different kinds. Fresh food-stuffs were often quite unobtainable. This restriction of diet to preserved foods frequently resulted, sooner or later, in outbreaks of scurvy, a disease which, while not among the most dangerous, nevertheless caused great suffering and inconvenience. That the trouble was actually caused by the nature of the diet was well recognised, because the disease could generally be stopped and remedied by a supply of fresh food, especially fresh vegetable food. Almost any such addition to the food supply was effective, and one of the commonest plants of our sea-coasts obtained the name of "scurvy grass" because of its supposed pre-eminence as a specific against scurvy, although actually there is no reason to suppose it is more valuable in this respect than many other plants. To the sailors it seemed so, because, growing near the sea, it was often the first available green food and as such, and for no special reason, benefited those suffering from scurvy. Doubtless almost any other plant would in similar circumstances have been equally valuable. We can see to-day that the explanation of the value of green food in this way is because it contains a particular vitamin, called vitamin C, which is anti-scorbutic, that is to say, prevents by its presence the disease scurvy, which is very liable to appear in its absence. This vitamin is widely present in fresh foods, especially vegetable foods, and since these are part of every normal diet the absence of the vitamin is not felt and scurvy is rare.

Another disease called beri-beri, which is common in parts

of tropical eastern Asia, is also generally supposed to be the result of absence from the diet of another vitamin, vitamin B. Beri-beri occurs chiefly among peoples whose diets, like those of some of the peoples of India, are almost entirely restricted to polished rice. If, however, a proportion of unpolished rice, that is to say the grain from which the husk has not been removed, is included in the diet the disease does not occur. Here the explanation is usually supposed to be that the necessary vitamin resides in the husk of the rice, and that if this is removed a vitamin deficiency results.

Numerous other examples might be given, but only one more can be mentioned here. Rickets in small children appears to be due to the absence from their food of certain vitamin-containing commodities, especially animal fats, such as are present in fresh milk and butter. In the absence of two vitamins which such substances contain, the bones of the body do not harden properly and growth is stunted. Rickets can be prevented and to some extent remedied by ensuring that the diet does include sufficient natural fats. One particular animal fat that contains these necessary vitamins, A and D, in comparatively large quantities is cod-liver oil, and this substance is now recognised as of very great value in the treatment and prevention of rickets and other deficiency troubles. It is interesting to observe that, long before vitamins were discovered, cod-liver oil was realised to be a valuable substance in early life although the reason was not understood.

These are some of the more familiar examples of vitamins. All the members of the class are, like the proteins, carbohydrates and fats, found naturally only in living or recently dead organic bodies. Although common in both plants and animals it is probable, as will be more apparent later, that they are all, indirectly at least, derived from plants. Our normal diets contain so wide a range of food-stuffs of all kinds that vitamin deficiency is never felt in the ordinary course of events, but it is well to remember that these important substances are especially abundant in fresh food of all kinds, especially green food, and that cooking and preservation tends to destroy them, or at any rate to impair their efficiency.

Now let us review once more the six classes of food materials. If we do this we shall see that there is about them a peculiarity which, though familiar enough, is nevertheless very remarkable. Four out of the six, including all the three large classes, are found in plant and animal bodies only. The other two, salts and water, are not restricted to plant and animal bodies but occur therein and most of the necessary supplies for food purposes come from thence. It would, as we have seen, be quite possible for some animals to live without absorbing any salt or water beyond that contained in the rest of their food. Even human beings could, if necessary, adjust their diets so as to include nothing but material derived from other living or recently killed bodies. In short, plants and animals can supply all necessary food-stuffs, and the very great majority of these food-stuffs can be obtained from no other source.

Even this statement is not a true summary of the position and a still more remarkable fact will be seen if we go a little further into the question. Most of us, at some period of our lives, have played the old game "animal, vegetable or mineral", and in so doing have, unconsciously perhaps, borne witness to the truth that any material object must belong to one or other of these three great categories or kingdoms of nature. The aspect of the kingdoms most important for examination here is the relative amounts of material they contain. It is pretty clear after a little consideration that bulk for bulk, the plant world must contain a good deal more than the animal world, since plants, although perhaps individually less bulky than the larger animals, often grow in close contact with one another over very wide areas. But the material comprised even in the plant kingdom is totally insignificant compared with that contained within the mineral kingdom, which includes not only the whole globe itself, but its waters and atmosphere also. Compared with the other two the material of the mineral kingdom must be considered practically incalculable.

Remember also that it is very much of the same kind as that in the living kingdoms in so far that it is made up of just the same fundamental substances or elements; so that not only has the mineral kingdom immensely more material than the others, but it is material of the same ingredients. Yet, and this is the extraordinary statement to which we have been leading, no appreciable amount of this vast store can be used directly as animal food—all this must come from the two comparatively tiny organic kingdoms themselves. As has been so long realised, stones are no substitute for bread.

Having made so definite a statement it will be as well to anticipate doubts by referring shortly to what are generally, but usually incorrectly, called "synthetic foods". The fact of the matter is that certain of the simpler chemical substances found naturally in food have been synthesised in the laboratory; but synthesis in the laboratory is a very different thing from manufacture on a commercial scale, and as far as the writer is aware this has never been done for any of them. It is even questionable, often, whether the synthesised substance is really identical in nutritive value with the natural one. It is true that the word "synthetic" is applied to certain marketable products, but it will be generally found that this merely means that the commodity has been artificially prepared from some plant or animal raw material. Such processes do not include the all-important change of material from inorganic to organic.

But if the food of animals comes from other living beings the further question now arises—whence comes the food of these other organisms? At this point it is convenient to treat animals and plants separately and first to discuss the food of animals other than human beings. The first fact to note is that the food requirements of all animals, whether human or not, are exactly the same. All animals need their food to be supplied in the six forms which we have described above and our particular human nutrition is not, in fact, essentially different from that of the lower animals. All animals obtain their food ultimately from the same source and that source is the plant kingdom.

A little thought is perhaps necessary before the truth of this is realised. A great deal of human food is clearly of animal origin; it is the direct or indirect product of animal bodies. Such foods, for example, as butter, milk, poultry, eggs and cheese are of this kind. But the animals which provide them are able to do so only because they have been nourished themselves by their particular food. Hence the cow provides milk and other foods in virtue of the fact that it has itself fed on certain other foods. These in the case of the cow are purely vegetable. Items of human diet like milk and cheese are therefore quite clearly derived indirectly from plant bodies. It is inevitable since the cow is a vegetarian. Just the same thing is seen whatever animal food is considered. As a matter of fact human animal food is a comparatively simple instance of the ultimate importance of the plant kingdom as the source of food, because humans are yet predominantly vegetarian and even when they eat animal food it is from animals which are themselves herbivorous. We do not as a rule eat carnivorous animals (certain fish are the chief exceptions). On the other hand, many of the higher animals, and especially the mammals, are definitely carnivorous and may even live on other carnivores. Here the dependence on plant food is not quite so clear. Yet the relationship is only a more indirect one. One carnivore may devour another and this in turn may devour a third, but sooner or later there will be devoured a herbivorous animal which lives directly upon plants. Let us take an example. Charles Darwin once pointed out that the power of clover to set seed depended to some extent upon the number of cats in the neighbourhood —an apparently quite irrelevant fact. His explanation was that the cats fed upon mice; that the mice often killed humble-bees; and that the clover was pollinated, that is to say set seed, as a result of visits from humble-bees. Hence if there were fewer cats the mice would flourish, there would be a high mortality among bees, the clover would therefore be visited less frequently and less seed would be set. Darwin's object was to illustrate the interdependence of living things, but the illustration is equally valuable as indicating the ultimate dependence of animals on plants. The mice form some of the food of the cats; the bees form some of the food of the mice; the clover provides, in its honey, food for the bees. If the clover failed to grow there would be no honey for the bees, no bees for the mice and no mice for the cats, and if the different animals were restricted to the particular food mentioned they would starve.

Many other examples of the same thing are more familiar even if they are less striking, but space does not permit of their mention here. The case of marine fish-food must, however, be explained briefly, because the plant relation is here especially obscured. Just as with life on the land so life in the sea includes carnivorous animals, herbivorous animals and plants. The plants, however, which form the food of the animals in the sea are usually not like land plants but are microscopic plants found floating on or near the surface of the water. These small plants (plankton) occur in enormous numbers and form the sole food of a great many small marine animals. These animals in turn form the food of small fishes and these in their turn are the food of many of the larger·fishes. The actual fishes which we eat are all finally dependent upon the floating plant life of the sea. The larger plants of the sea, the sea-weeds that grow so thickly along the shore, are actually of very little importance compared with the minute floating plants.

Thus we see that wherever we may look we always find that animals, no matter of what kind, are dependent in the end upon plants for their existence. We may enjoy our breakfast bacon, but we should do so with due acknowledgements of our indebtedness to the vegetarian habits of the pig, and to the providence which has provided it with sufficient vegetable matter on which to grow corpulent. We may esteem roast grouse, but we should rather esteem the heather and other plants of its native moors which have enabled it to reach the plump condition.

Chapter III

THE LIFE OF THE GREEN PLANT

It was seen in the preceding chapter that certain substances only are of use as human food: that these substances also form the food of all other animals: and that all animals, human and otherwise, obtain these substances directly or indirectly from plants. What then are the food-stuffs of plants and whence does the plant obtain them?

The first part of the question is easily answered. The food substances of plants are exactly those already described for animals. In fact the food of all living things is the same, for the simple reason that all living things make exactly the same use of their food. Let us consider what these uses are. They are twofold. In the first place some of the food absorbed has to be used for building up new body material in growth or for replacing or repairing body tissues. But the making of the living body substances requires a great deal of energy and so, in the second place, some food has to be used for the production of this necessary energy which will be needed for the carrying out of the process of growth and body repair. A very simple, but, at the same time, fairly adequate illustration of this twofold use of food can be given by comparing a living body with one of the concrete mixers which are to-day so familiar a sight wherever new roads are being constructed. If a concrete mixer is watched in action it will be seen that, by the aid of some kind of mechanical energy, supplied usually by an engine of some sort, the machinery of the mixer revolves and in so doing mixes the ingredients of the concrete so that they are finally presented as a completely manufactured product. The actual method by which this mixing is done does not concern us here, just as in practice it probably does not concern the people who actually use the concrete. What is important is to notice that, for the machine to function properly, two things must be supplied, the ingredients of the concrete and the energy by which they can be mixed into the finished article. Only when these two requirements are met in proper proportion and amount will the mixer perform its proper function. The relation of food and living bodies is almost exactly parallel and the working of a living organism is in many ways very like that of a concrete mixer. In each a particular product is desired, on the one hand concrete and on the other new body building material: in each the mechanism, the mixer and the body, is present but will not and cannot function unless certain things are supplied to it. In the mixer, these are first the ingredients of the concrete and secondly fuel for the production of energy by the engine; in the body, they are first the ingredients of new body material and secondly fuel to supply the energy by which these ingredients can be mixed into actual building substances. In the body, part of the food provides the first and part provides the second and this is the meaning of the twofold function of food. The first process, that of the building-up of material, we call assimilation, the second, that of energy production, we call respiration. The corresponding processes in the concrete mixer are the mixing of the ingredients in the machine and the utilisation of the fuel in the engine.

This homely illustration will, it is hoped, explain why the food of all living things is so much the same. It is because every living thing has to do the same two things, namely, respire and build its body, and the reason why it can do the latter only with very definite kinds of food is that the actual living substance of all organisms is the same—protoplasm.

This answers the question—what are the foods of plants? They are the same as those of animals. But here is a problem. Animals, as has been shown, obtain all their food directly or indirectly from plants. Whence, then, do the plants obtain theirs? Clearly they do not obtain it from animals and equally clearly they can scarcely obtain it from one another. That would be like the people who are said to live by taking in each other's washing. There must obviously be some way in which plants differ fundamentally from animals.

In general this difference is familiar enough to students of botany but it may be that some details of it are not quite clear. Apart from this it is so fundamentally important that no apology is needed for emphasising it once again here. The difference is this—the great majority of plants do not require that their foods shall be presented to them ready made, that is to say as carbohydrates, fats, proteins and vitamins, but they are able to manufacture these comparatively complex substances themselves from the very simple raw materials that can be supplied by the mineral world. The result of this peculiar power of the plant is something so vast as to be difficult to realise. Without it the vegetable and animal kingdoms would disappear and with them the human race.

This statement is such a drastic one that it deserves some detailed consideration. First of all, this ability of plants means that the plant kingdom forms the one and only connecting link between the kingdoms of living things and the mineral world. It was pointed out earlier that the immense resources of the mineral world were of no direct use whatever in the provision of animal food because no animals are able to live on the substances found in it or to manufacture food from them. The plant, like the animal, cannot use mineral substances directly as food but it *can manufacture*, from mineral substances, the foods which it needs. Thus through the medium of the plant, the animal world is put in a position to make use of the great stores of matter bound up in the mineral world. From this it follows that as long as there are sufficient plants there can be no question of food shortage. In rather more precise terms the production of human food is limited only by the difficulties of growing or exploiting sufficient plants. The failure of a vegetable crop or the failure to exploit a vegetable source is the failure of a potential portion, however small, of the world's food supply.

But the picture is not quite complete yet. We have seen that the plant can utilise, in manufacturing food, materials drawn directly from the mineral world and that this food once made is used by animals. Does this mean that there is a continual and uncompensated drainage of raw materials from the mineral world so that some day even this source may become exhausted? The answer to the question is an emphatic "no", based upon two lines of argument. The first is the principle of the conservation of matter, but far more immediately important than this, which might not be effective till far too late biologically, is the series of events in nature, embodied in the words "putrefaction" or "decay".

The living plant or animal body may in one sense be visualised as a collection of many proteins, carbohydrates, fats and sundry other classes of compounds too numerous to mention, organised in such a manner that they exhibit in concert the phenomenon of life. When the individual dies this organisation, whatever it may exactly be, ceases and the body is merely a heterogeneous mass of chemical substances. It may be that they will contribute to the food of one of the higher animals and will then be obviously consumed, but if this does not happen nevertheless they will sooner or later disappear. This "disappearance" is the process known as putrefaction, but the word is an inconvenient one. There is actually no essential difference between the consumption of a dead body in the course of, let us say, a lion's meal and its disappearance by "putrefaction". The only distinction is that while in the one a single high grade animal is concerned, in the other the active agents are myriads of those minute organisms, the bacteria, putrefaction being simply the outward and visible (generally olfactory also) sign of their ordinary nutritive activities.

The vital importance of putrefaction lies in the facts that, on the whole, the substances that bacteria absorb as food are a good deal simpler than those actually found in fresh dead bodies: that the bacteria produce special substances (enzymes) in order to convert the one into the other: and that they respire actively also, oxidising many substances in the process. The combined result of all this is that from the time when the bacteria first appear the dead body disintegrates rapidly by enzyme action and oxidation. One kind of bacteria is followed by another as the breaking down continues until finally their food supply fails and decay is complete. Throughout this period all kinds of chemical changes are taking place in the dead body and all sorts of substances are formed, some of them very offensive to the human nose, but slowly and surely simpler and simpler substances are being produced, until finally the once-living creature has been disintegrated into almost exactly the same constituents as those from which it was originally built up.

So it is that by the activities of the bacteria, and to some extent also of other animals, the inorganic material built up by the activity of plants into living tissues is not thereby permanently lost, but will in due time return to its original condition. There may be, as is only to be expected, leaks in the circuit, but for all practical purposes they are trivial and it may be said that there is a constant cycle of the elements in organic nature. This is the reason why the activities of plants are not likely to exhaust the available supplies of material in the inorganic world.

We must now return to our main theme and see how the nutrition of plants is effected.

In one way at least, to grow plants is a much simpler business than to grow animals. Once a plant is set in the soil in the air it is unnecessary to supply it with any food, it is quite capable of obtaining by itself all that it needs. But it has been said that the actual food-stuffs of plants and animals are the same, and that the plant can manufacture these foods from certain simple mineral raw materials. It is clear then that these raw materials must be such as can be obtained by the plant from its surroundings. These surroundings are the air and the soil, and so it follows that the raw materials for the building-up of food must come from those sources. Actually the plant takes in from the soil liquids only, namely the water in the soil, together with various substances in solution in that water, and these together form an important part of its raw food materials. But it also takes in from the air a gas called carbon dioxide which is present everywhere in the atmosphere in small but fairly constant proportion. This forms the second part of its raw food materials. Thus the plant absorbs three supplies, first the water in the soil, secondly the salts in solution in that water, and thirdly the carbon dioxide in the air. From these three the plant is able to build up all the four most important classes of its foods—the proteins, the carbohydrates, the fats and the vitamins. Water and salts are taken up as such. We must now see how this actual food building is done.

The preliminary and most essential process in the general manufacture of food by the plant is the building up of simple carbohydrates from the carbon dioxide of the air and water from the soil. These two substances are combined in some mysterious way in the leaves of the plant into certain simple kinds of sugars, which are some of the least complex kinds of carbohydrates. Once these substances are formed the later stages of food manufacture are fairly straightforward. The necessary carbohydrates are formed and from them are derived fats, and further, by the addition of some of the mineral salts taken in with the water of the soil, proteins are formed. Similarly vitamins also make their appearance, but we as yet know so little of the chemistry of this class of substances that it is not possible to suggest exactly how they are made. One thing clear is that the first process results in the formation of sugars and that from these the other three classes are later made. In this way all the six classes of food-stuffs are provided. It will be seen that there are several processes before all the requirements are satisfied, but it will be quite evident that the crucial stage is the manufacture of sugars from carbon dioxide and water. This is the vital process by which the purely mineral substances from the air and the soil are made to form part of the actual body of the plant and in virtue of which the plant becomes the connecting link between the mineral world and the world of living things.

If the reader were asked what he or she considered the most striking peculiarity of plants in general the answer would probably be their green colour, and this answer would undoubtedly be the right one. Green is a very common colour in nature but only because of the abundance of vegetation. Apart from plants, green is a very rare colour in living things or in minerals. It might, then, be supposed with reason that the presence of this green colour in plants, and not in other things, has some important connection with that outstanding feature of plants which is their ability to manufacture their own food. This is indeed the case. It is only those plants which contain green colouring matter that are able to do this. The actual colouring is caused by a substance called chlorophyll, a word simply meaning "leaf-green". In the presence of chlorophyll, and only in the presence of chlorophyll, can food manufacture go on. There are some plants which have no chlorophyll—mushrooms and toadstools are familiar examples—and these plants cannot make their own food. The very great majority of plants, however, are green and can therefore combine carbon dioxide and water into simple sugars.

We do not yet know exactly how this combination is effected but we have some general idea. Something else besides chlorophyll is necessary, namely energy, for the actual process. This energy is obtained from the light of the sun and sugar manufacture goes on only in light. Apparently what happens is that, by the aid of chlorophyll, the plant is able to absorb energy from sunlight in such a way as to make it capable of bringing about the combination of carbon dioxide and water rapidly, and this is really all that can be said about the process in the present state of our knowledge. We do know that four things are necessary, carbon dioxide, water, chlorophyll and sunlight, but exactly how they interact is not clear. The most important fact from the point of view of practical human affairs is that no human being has ever succeeded in imitating the process outside the green plant. Some investigators have succeeded in obtaining small traces of sugars from carbon dioxide and water with special kinds of energy, but the conditions under which this has been done are so unlike those which presumably exist in the plant, and the actual amount of sugars contained is so small that, to all intents and purposes, the only method of obtaining sugars is by the process which goes on in the living plant. With all our knowledge of chemistry and biology we are ourselves as yet quite unable to make sugar on a commercial scale.

It is difficult at first to realise the immense significance of this, especially from the point of view of the welfare of the human race. Let us reiterate certain facts. First, population depends entirely and directly on an adequate supply of food. Second, this supply must be made up of certain definite substances. Third, these are obtainable almost exclusively only from living things, and mineral substances are practically useless. Fourth, the only living things capable of making them are green plants. Fifth, their manufacture depends entirely upon the chemical process by which carbon dioxide and water are combined into sugars in the leaf of the plant, and this process cannot be imitated.

The conclusion to be drawn from these facts is clear. It is that our human food supplies, and those of other animals as well, are available only as the result of chemical processes going on in the leaves of green plants. We cannot replace the processes and, therefore, we cannot control our ultimate supplies of food to any appreciable extent. All that we can do is to try and increase those supplies by augmenting the amount of vegetable matter in the world, that is to say by cultivating plants as crops. We are really dependent for our welfare on the maintenance of sufficient agricultural production. In fact, we depend upon chemical reactions which we do not fully understand and which we cannot properly control. All that we can do is to provide the maximum opportunities for them—a slender enough thread on which to hang the fabric of human economics.

These conclusions lead to a very natural question. Will man succeed in solving the mystery of the manufacture of sugar by the plant and so be able to replace the natural process by an artificial one capable of being controlled at will, or not? It is very difficult to give an answer because so much depends on the real nature of the process and this is not at present clear. If the process is purely and simply a chemical one merely requiring certain conditions which have not yet been discovered, it seems likely that the problem will be solved and at some not far distant date. If, on the other hand, the process in the plant goes on in virtue of the life of the plant, that is to say, if it can go on only in the living plant and in presence of life, success is not so sure because the solution of the problem may involve a knowledge of the nature of life which may well be unattainable. In any case success or failure is a matter of the future. For the present, at least, we are at the mercy of the plant and although efforts are constantly being made to remedy this the day of success is not yet at hand. Until then our activities must be directed towards lessening our dependence as much as possible, by increasing our knowledge of how to cultivate plants to the best advantage and how to overcome the factors which tend to limit the amount and supply of vegetable foods.

Chapter IV

FACTORS LIMITING AGRICULTURAL PRODUCTION

Ever since the earliest times the human population of the world has been steadily increasing and, in the last few hundred years, that increase has, by the elimination of such causes of destruction as famine and pestilence, assumed relatively enormous proportions. It is estimated that the population of Europe has multiplied fourfold in the last two hundred years. At the present time the population of the world is calculated at about 1850 millions, a figure that is thought to be twice that of a century ago, and it is anticipated that, unless some radical change occurs, a similar doubling will take place by the end of this century. These figures are so vast that they actually convey very little, but the rates and proportions of increase are comprehensible enough. They demonstrate one fact beyond dispute, namely, that since man is dependent on plants for so much of his well-being, increase of population has always meant increased demands for the products of the plant world, and that the more rapid the rate of population increase the more exacting become these demands. Hence there has always existed a need for increases in plant production and exploitation but, in the last few centuries, and especially in the last century, it has become much more essential. As the world population approaches the maximum so this necessity will become greater and greater, and to-day mankind is rapidly approaching the state of affairs when, for the first time, population increase will threaten to outrun the rate of increase in agricultural production and when further human increase will depend greatly on the possibility of augmenting the existing food supplies.

At first sight it would seem a comparatively simple matter to increase agricultural production to almost any desired extent. Unfortunately there are a great many considerations which hinder this and which tend to limit the maximum production of the world or portions of it.

It is very important before proceeding further to have a sound knowledge of at least the more important of these, and they are described in this chapter. The list makes no claim to be complete and there are doubtless many minor factors unmentioned. These it must be left to the reader to think out. It is convenient to consider the different factors separately, but it must be remembered that only rarely is one factor independent of others. Normally they are all so closely related that any practical effect is clearly the result of the interaction of several.

Perhaps the most obvious limiting factor is space. The growing of crops involves the use of great areas of land and it often happens, for this reason alone, that a country cannot produce enough food for its inhabitants from within its own boundaries. Great Britain is, in some ways at least, a good example of this. The staple food commodity of our people is wheat, and the amount of wheat grown in this country is only a small fraction of the total requirement of the population. At the same time wheat is a crop which will grow perfectly well, as far as soil and climatic conditions are concerned, in many parts of our country. Indeed the yield of grain *per acre* in Britain is higher than in any other part of the world. One reason why we depend so much on imports for our wheat is certainly because there is not enough space available in which to grow, economically, all that we need. Although, as has just been said, much of this country is suitable for wheat growing, much of it is not, and of the former only a certain amount can be spared for the purpose. Our diet is a very mixed one, and even if wheat is the most important item in it there are many other things, such as meat, which are almost equally desirable. As a result the acreage under wheat or available for that crop is small and quite inadequate. There is no doubt that, under certain economic conditions, this could be increased, but in normal circumstances a small supply is all that we can grow. In countries like Canada, on the other hand, the reverse condition obtains. The actual yield of wheat per acre is very much smaller, but such vast areas are available and suitable for growing it that far more is produced than is consumed in the country and Canada actually exports more wheat than any other country in the world. With such overseas sources of supply as these at our disposal the inducement and necessity of growing more wheat at home is not much felt and the increase of home production is not imperative. Actually the home supply is diminishing slightly from year to year, but given greater space our production would doubtless be much higher.

The importance of space as a factor in agriculture will be more easily realised if we consider some actual figures in relation to our own country. The total area of Great Britain is approximately 88,000 square miles or 56 million acres. Excluding rough pasture land, which covers about 15 million acres, the amount under agricultural cultivation is about 30 million acres or some 53 per cent. of the whole. Of these 30 million acres something less than one-half is arable land, something more than one-half is permanent grassland. The figures are actually 13 millions and 17 millions respectively. The arable land is divided up among the principal crops in the following manner. Cereals as a class occupy about 44 per cent., or rather less than half, of which wheat and barley each occupy one-quarter and oats the rest. Beans and peas account for just over 2 per cent., potatoes 5 per cent., roots 10 per cent., clover and grasses nearly 30 per cent., orchards and small fruits about $2\frac{1}{2}$ per cent., and the rest is divided up among the remaining crops. As we have seen, we grow at home about one-fifth of our wheat and this occupies just over 10 per cent. of the total arable land. In order to supply our whole wheat requirements at least one-half of the total arable area would have to be utilised, and this would mean a drastic reduction in other crops. More than this it is fairly certain that much of the land under other crops would not grow wheat so well, and it is at least questionable whether it would be possible, even if convenient, to grow all the wheat we need. The problem is largely that of parcelling out the available land among different crops in the most convenient and economic way and, while that is the consideration, it is probably not possible to increase our home wheat yield to any great extent. Wheat has been taken here as a particularly familiar and important food but the same restrictions apply to other crops, and one thing is quite certain, that there is not enough space in this country to provide all the food requirements of the population. Any increased production of one or more would inevitably mean a lessened production of others.

The problem of space is closely connected with the fact that many crop plants require very definite conditions of soil and climate for successful growth. Even if Great Britain were a much larger country we should still have to be dependent upon imports for many of our foods simply because they cannot be grown at home. The three common beverages—tea, coffee and cocoa—are good examples of this. All three are obtained from tropical plants which need very warm conditions for their growth, and however desirous we might be of producing them at home, we should be quite unable to do so. The peculiar needs of certain crops have another serious economic effect, namely, that supplies of them are restricted to comparatively few parts of the world. This, for various reasons of a political nature, may have a profound influence on the amount and facility of supply.

Yet another aspect of the space problem is that of the differences in productivity in different parts of the world. Some regions are notoriously more fertile than others. The outstanding examples of this are, perhaps, the valley of the Nile and the Mediterranean countries, where good climatic conditions go hand-in-hand with good soils. It is no chance that has made these regions the great centres of civilisation in the past. Other great areas like the hot deserts of northern

Africa and the cold deserts of central Asia are definitely unsuitable for plant cultivation and exploitation. As a result they
support but meagre populations and contribute little to the
total production of the world.

A second factor of great importance is that of time. With
any crop an appreciable time must elapse between the setting
of the seed and the harvesting of the crop. Even the most
rapidly maturing crops take at least some weeks to reach
maturity, and hence it is not possible to correct suddenly an
actual or threatened food shortage by further planting.
Sowing must be done in ignorance of the actual conditions
which will exist when the crop is ready, and in most cases the
harvest cannot be delayed to meet special economic requirements. A generation or two ago the difficulties resulting from
this were much greater than they are now, and the harvest of
certain fruits illustrates this well. In those days many fruits,
such as apples, were cultivated almost exclusively in the
northern hemisphere and predominantly in the old world. The
harvest in the different growing regions came at about the
same time, and there was a tendency for apples to be plentiful
at some seasons and unobtainable at others, except in so far as
they were capable of being stored. Nowadays apples are grown
not only throughout the northern hemisphere but also in many
parts of the southern hemisphere. In the latter the time of
ripening alternates with that of the north, and so there is a
more or less constant supply of apples from one source or
another on the market, those of the different areas arriving in
succession. It is partly the spread of fruit-growing to the
south that has made possible the great increase in the consumption of many fruits.

Some plants come to maturity comparatively quickly, as
for example, most annual crops like the grains, and sometimes
it is possible to obtain two crops in one year, but many plants,
especially trees, take many years to reach a state of productivity. This has a considerable economic bearing because the
capital invested in their cultivation is locked up and un-

productive for long periods. There is also the human element, that everyone likes to see the results of his labours and there is a natural reluctance to cultivate crops which may not mature in the lifetime of the planter. Actually few, if any, important food plants are in this category, but the difficulty is rather prominent in forestry. It is to some extent for this reason that the planting of hard-wood trees, like the oak, has declined and been superseded by the planting of the much more rapidly maturing soft-wood trees like the pines and the larches. The inferiority of their wood for certain purposes is compensated by their quicker yield.

Some crops can be stored much more easily than others. Grains fortunately are among the former and cereal farming does not present difficulties in this direction. Many other foods, however, can scarcely be stored at all, as is the case with most vegetables and fruits, and so these are usually grown only when and where there is a reasonable prospect of the immediate consumption of the harvest. Foods like these cannot be kept to await a favourable market, and their cultivation is doubtless adversely affected by this disability.

Both these factors of space and time are intimately associated with the difficulties of labour, and the problem of labour is certainly one of the greatest immediate and actual limiting factors in the production of food. The Great War offered a striking illustration of one aspect of this. During the years 1914–18 considerable areas of Great Britain were made to bear human food crops for the first time for many years. In ordinary times the cost of cultivating them was, for various reasons, so high as to be unremunerative and they were therefore generally left to rough pasture. The necessity for greater food production at home in the war years was so vital that cost of production was a subsidiary consideration which was met by some kind of government aid. With this assistance, or by reason of greatly raised war prices, crop growing became possible in many places where it was formerly impossible, but as soon as the war ended and the emergency passed, assistance was withdrawn or prices fell and further cultivation in these regions became once more uneconomic and they relapsed into their former condition. In this case the actual cost of production was, and is, the limiting factor, but this cost is chiefly that of paying the necessary labour for the long periods during which the crops are growing, and this is true of most agriculture.

Another factor which is often of very considerable importance is the difficulty of obtaining sufficient labour at an economic rate. The economics of agriculture in most countries is such that agricultural labourers can be paid only a small wage in comparison with many other callings and there is frequently a difficulty in recruiting the ranks for this reason.

The actual work too is onerous and the hours necessarily long and without many of the compensations in other walks of life. Probably this particular aspect of our food supply and its maintenance is not very familiar, but in point of fact it has given rise to many historical events of the first magnitude. It is not fantastic, for example, to attribute to it some of the astonishingly rapid onset of the industrial revolution at the beginning of the last century. The new avenues of industrial employment which then opened offered many inducements in comparison with agriculture.

But there are other instances of the relation between agricultural labour and historical events which, although they do not actually concern food substances, are nevertheless of great interest. Civilised man is perhaps seen at his vilest in some of his dealings with those races of the human family which have not had his advantages and which he thinks are his inferiors. Certainly some of the most disgraceful episodes in history are those associated with the enslavement of primitive peoples, and more often than not the underlying cause of it has been a botanical one. Three cases may be cited from the history of the last hundred years. By the beginning of this period there had developed the great trade in slaves between tropical Africa and North America and by the middle of the century the resultant situation was largely responsible for the great civil

war between the northern and southern states of North
America. Whatever may have been the actual causes of the
struggle it soon resolved itself into one between the people
who wished to continue the slave system and those who wished
it to be abolished. A whole continent suffered a civil war of
terrible intensity before victory came, at long last, to the slave
emancipators. The important point for us is that the whole
slave trade and its attendant evils hinged to a great degree upon
the cultivation of cotton in the southern States. Only by the
employment of unpaid slave labour was it possible to make the
cotton-growing industry flourish in the way its owners
wished and hence, as a direct result of what was, in fact, a
difficulty of obtaining cheap agricultural labour, developed all
the mischief.

The more recent example of the Belgian Congo is much the
same. In the forests of that part of Africa certain rubber-
producing trees were abundant and their exploitation quickly
assumed large dimensions. But the business of sending collectors out into the forests to secure the rubber was costly and
wasteful, so much so as to react upon the prospects of the industry. The result was recourse to the abundant native labour
available by the impressment of the native population, and
there rapidly developed a situation indistinguishable from some
forms of slavery except in name. Fortunately international
opinion was more educated and potent than in earlier generations and the exposure of the facts was sufficient to lead to
their reform.

The third example was very like that just described and
concerned the exploitation of wild rubber in parts of tropical
South America. Here again the duration of the evil conditions
of labour was fortunately short. Besides these instances of
cotton and rubber the same kind of thing occurred at one time
in the cultivation of cocoa in western tropical Africa.

Another subject that is closely connected with labour and
cost of production is that of over-production. The cost of
agricultural practice often determines that crops can be pro-

duced at a profit only when the actual market price of the commodity is above a certain figure, and it is sometimes necessary or desirable to maintain this figure artificially. If a large supply of the commodity is placed carelessly on the market it may become so abundant that its price must be reduced in order to ensure its sale. It then may happen that the price falls below that economic figure at which production is profitable. When this happens a producer is liable to find that the price eventually obtained is not enough to cover the cost of production, a cost which must be met before the market at the time of harvest is ascertainable. This has resulted not infrequently in the taking of definite steps to prevent an un-limited supply of a commodity from coming suddenly on the market. These steps may be satisfactory from the point of view of the producer since his prices have been maintained, but the consumer may be denied the advantages of a drop in prices. Sometimes food supplies have even been destroyed to prevent them becoming, from the producer's point of view, a drug on the market. Whether this is a defensible or inevitable practice must be left for economists to decide.

In the present circumstances of food production and supply, when the requirements of one country are often met from sources all over the world, the factors of transport and pre-servation are of great importance. A given food-stuff may be produced in good quantity and quality in some part of the world, but before it can be placed within reach of the consumer the cost of its transport may raise its market price to impossible levels. Actually it is usually possible to foresee such a situation and unnecessary production can be prevented, but this factor certainly tends to limit the growing of certain crops in certain places. There is little doubt that many regions would grow quantities of additional commodities were it not for this draw-back, which makes them unable to compete with countries more favourably situated. That the limitation is not more obvious is due to the careful organisation of the world's production areas.

A difficulty more widely felt is that of preserving foods in the course of their transfer from producer to consumer. If the areas of cultivation and marketing are widely separated geographically there is often a difficulty in getting produce to market in a fresh condition. A great deal has been done recently to overcome this. The banana trade, for example, has increased enormously since the provision of ships specially designed to carry the fruit without injury and equipped so that it can be loaded in an unripe condition and allowed to ripen during the voyage. Similarly the increased knowledge of cold storage and refrigeration has added to our home markets several edibles which previously could not be brought from overseas without damage or loss. Despite this there are still many plant products, like certain tropical fruits, which will not stand lengthy travel and which are therefore unavailable here at home. No doubt a time will come when even these will be transported successfully, but the difficulty is likely to remain for some time and while it does certain regions cannot play their full part in food supply however suitable their conditions may be.

Finally there are two factors controlling the production of food-stuffs which are rather different from those already mentioned. They are the devastation of growing or harvested crops by disease or pests, and by weather.

It is difficult for any one not personally concerned with plant growing to realise the great prevalence of disease among plants of all kinds. It is probably true to say that there is not a single plant crop that is not liable to injury or destruction from at least one disease and often from more than one. Sometimes the disease is the result of insect pests, but more often it is caused by the attack of some parasitic plant, usually a fungus. Whichever may be the cause it is no exaggeration to say that disease is the greatest danger to food production that exists. Great strides have been made towards the prevention and control of such diseases in recent years, but the danger is still a very pressing one. On several occasions a whole promising industry has been destroyed by this cause, as happened not so long ago in the case of coffee growing in Ceylon. We saw, too, in an earlier chapter how disease destroyed the potato crops of Ireland in the eighteen-forties and although such far-reaching effects are rare, lesser ones are still common. Even in England at the present time crops are periodically reduced or spoilt by the onset of disease which cannot be successfully combated, and the same thing is seen even more frequently in the tropics where our knowledge of the destructive agencies is less complete. It is certain that, could the total harmful effects of plant diseases and insect pests be estimated, they would be found to have a very serious limiting effect on the world supply of plant products.

The danger of harmful weather conditions is much the same as that of disease, and they are often connected, but in the case of weather, man is even more helpless. With all his scientific knowledge the weather is still almost entirely beyond his control, and we in this country need no reminder that a spell of bad weather at a critical period of plant growth may spell ruination to the harvest. The two greatest dangers are excessive rain and excessive drought. Both are serious but the latter, as we know, is, in most countries, commoner. The agriculturalist is generally quite unable to take any steps either to prevent or remedy the ill-effects, except, perhaps, by irrigation, and he is in a very real sense at the mercy of the elements. Frost, too, is in many places a great danger. Man's influence over the earth which he inhabits may be profound, but the weather has not yet come within his sphere of influence and he can only hope for the best while anticipating the worst.

Chapter V

SCIENCE AND AGRICULTURE

The serious consequences of the factors limiting agricultural production have long been realised, and all the forces of science have been marshalled to meet and minimise them. It is, however, perhaps not generally realised how successful these efforts have been and how much mankind owes, especially in recent years, to the results of scientific investigation, and this chapter is devoted to a short account of some of the more outstanding ways in which science has helped to overcome these limitations of nature. Since the problems involved are, more often than not, botanical problems, it is not surprising that botanists have been the scientists chiefly concerned in them, but every branch of learning has been pressed into service and has performed its useful part.

Naturally enough the greatest factor in the increase of agricultural production has been the actual body of husbandry knowledge which has gradually grown up in the course of long experience. Agriculture, like most other aspects of human civilisation, has passed through a series of stages each characterised by the use of methods and processes better and more efficient than those which preceded them, and each representing a superior condition of knowledge. In its most primitive state, agriculture consists merely of sowing and harvesting sufficiently to meet immediate, comparatively small, requirements without any reference to the more distant future or to the ultimate effect on the soil. When space is abundant and population low this method is adequate, because as soon as one area of cultivation shows signs of exhaustion it is possible for the population to move to another. But if the population is to be stationary the problem becomes more difficult. Since plants obtain some of their essential raw food materials from the soil in which they grow, every crop removes from the soil some of the food materials it contains. The result is that after one crop has been grown in the same soil a number of times the ground tends to become exhausted, that is to say drained, of one or more of its constituents, and subsequent crops will have insufficient of this constituent for their needs and will therefore yield poorly. This soil exhaustion is a particularly serious matter where, because of space considerations, it is necessary to cultivate the same areas time after time without cessation. So serious, indeed, does the problem become that it is no exaggeration to say that nearly all the advances which have been made in methods of practical husbandry have been designed, indirectly or directly, to lessen its effect. The simplest and earliest method adopted was to allow a proportion of the land to lie fallow for a period, during which the naturally developing vegetation was not removed. This has the obvious disadvantage that the land so resting is unproductive, and the method is economically possible only when space is of little consideration and production need not be pressed to the limit. The next step was the discovery, or perhaps it would be more accurate to say the realisation, that different crops vary much in their effects upon the soil. Particularly is this true of the differential way in which crops exhaust the soil in which they grow. Some extract from it especially large amounts of certain salts while taking very little of others. Some take more of the latter and less of the former. Some even have a beneficial effect and in certain respects give more than they take. This is particularly the case with the members of the bean and pea family, the Leguminosae. Many of these plants bear on their roots small swellings caused by and containing .bacteria These bacteria have the power of collecting nitrogen from the air and of combining it into the nitrogenous compounds of their bodies. When the plant dies these roots decay and the contained bacterial bodies are liberated into the soil and add greatly to its value, a circumstance peculiarly fortunate since it is of nitrogen salts that soils most easily become exhausted. The value of leguminous plants in this way has long been realised even if not understood (Virgil refers to it in the *Georgics*) and the practice of growing a leguminous crop after a cereal, for example, because the former tended to restore to the soil just those constituents which the latter removed, originated very early. This, in very simple language, is the basis underlying the alternation of crops. Its advantage is great because, while the soil is recuperating, it is also producing and the cultivator is not faced with a barren period.

Thus began the great agricultural practice of crop rotation, the growing of definite and particular crops one after the other so that the demands of one on the soil tend to be counterbalanced by the others and the ultimate loss is much lessened. With experience the rotation of crops soon became more and more scientific until finally, with the introduction of root crops like turnips and beets, there developed in the eighteenth century the fourfold rotation of clover, wheat, turnips, barley. This rotation, commonly called the Norfolk rotation because it was first established in that county, has ever since been the basis of much of the agricultural procedure in this country as well as in other similarly situated regions.

Up to this time agricultural progress had all been towards extensive farming, that is, towards large-scale farms and operations. Extensive farming now seems to have reached its limits and recent developments have been all in the direction of intensive small-scale farming, that is, towards the increase of production per small area by various scientific means, like the use of chemical fertilisers, crop protection from weather, and so on, which would not be applicable over large areas. Certain countries like Denmark have developed intensive cultivation to a very marked extent. It is not, however, suitable for all crops and rather for those where the bulk of production is not the only or primary consideration. Intensive cultivation may not promise to supplant extensive farming, but in future there will probably grow up a fairer division between them.

A particular aspect of the development of agricultural practice has been the success achieved in the investigation of soils and of the conditions necessary for the successful cultivation of different crops. As a result of the knowledge so gained a great deal has been done to overcome the limitations of space by making soils, which were hitherto totally or partly unproductive, capable of yielding their maximum quota of crops. The subject of manuring, a very complicated one, has received especial attention, and it is now possible, by the use of proper fertilisers, to add the desired constituents to the soils which lack them and to restore them to soils which have become exhausted of them. In this way not only is the yield of regions already cultivated much increased but wide areas have, for the first time, been made capable of bearing crops. In a rather different way, too, other barren regions have been made fertile by the scientific use and conservation of water supplies in overcoming, at least locally, the grave disadvantages of a climate with insufficient rain. It is by such methods of irrigation that wide areas, as in Egypt, have been brought into cultivation. The recently completed Lloyd Barrage on the Indus in north-west India is said to be able to water an area of five million acres.

The collection and dissemination of scientific agricultural knowledge will always be one of the surest means of increasing crop production in the long run because, where ignorance prevails, it is inevitable that cultivation will be wasteful and incomplete. It is only by education of the right kind that slovenly and uneconomic methods can be eliminated and the earth be made to yield her proper increase. The production of the world as a whole would be much augmented if the cultivation of all parts of it could be carried on at one and the same high level of scientific knowledge, but a great deal of agriculture is, perforce, still reliant on the labour of primitive and uneducated people who have neither the opportunity nor the inclination to use better methods. Poverty, too, is both cause and effect. It is an invariable accompaniment of ignorance and means an inability to make use of modern processes. Very primitive kinds of cultivation still persist in many parts of the world and, while they do, the communities which practise them will also remain poor and primitive and unable to afford the equipment by which increased yield and wealth might be obtained. Education is by no means the least of the ways in which limitation of production can be lessened.

The limiting factor of labour and its cost is perhaps less susceptible to permanent improvement than some of the other factors, but the better knowledge of markets and the causes which control them, and of international trade and finance, as well as a better understanding between peoples, cannot fail to have a beneficial effect on the problem. Questions like these are the domain of the professional economist, and workers in this particular branch of science have played, and are playing, a great part in indicating the ways in which production and marketing can be improved and the difficulties of cost and labour diminished.

Such are some examples of the way in which the general question of the production and maintenance of our human food supplies and other plant products has been assisted by scientists other than botanists. The work of the botanists is of even greater value in that it concerns directly the well-being of the plants themselves, which are the basis of the economic structure.

Two aspects of botany, or rather of biology, since zoologists have also been largely concerned, have received special attention within recent years and have made advances of first-rate importance and value. These are the investigation of the improvement of crops by selection and breeding and the combating of plant diseases.

By selection is meant the gradual improvement of crops or strains or races by the simple method of continually sowing or propagating, generation after generation, only from the best and most worthy individuals of a harvest. Among any considerable numbers of living things of one and the same kind the individuals always tend to vary somewhat amongst themselves, just as human individuals are more or less unlike one another and vary in quality. If the new generation is grown from chosen individuals, that is to say, from individuals chosen because they exhibit in great degree desirable characters, there will be a tendency for those characters to appear slightly emphasised in the new generation. If once more the most conspicuous individuals as regards these characters are selected and bred from, the desired features are further accentuated in the next generation, and so on. After comparatively few generations of this process the value of the crop in the character selected is often immensely greater than that of the original stock. Such a selection has, for instance, been one of the chief methods in producing the relatively enormous flowers of some cultivated garden species. Sowings were made repeatedly only from the largest flowered individuals, and by this means the average size of flower has in many plants so increased that the relationship with their wild prototypes is almost unrecognisable.

Selection of this simple kind has been practised for a long time, but it has its limitations. The improved or selected forms are liable to revert to their original condition if selection is not maintained, and this is generally not possible after the varieties have been put on the market. Further it is impossible deliberately, merely by selection, to add to a race or strain a character which it does not already show. To take a very simple example. It would probably not be possible to produce from a yellow-flowered plant race a blue-flowered race because the former do not, in all likelihood, contain any potentiality for blue colour and no amount of ordinary selection will cause it to appear.

On the other hand, it may, and indeed frequently does, happen when large numbers of individuals are grown together that one of them may differ very markedly and peculiarly from the rest. Such a sudden and abnormal variant is called a mutation, or more popularly a "sport". Sports often show characters quite distinct from those appearing in the other individuals and are therefore made the starting point of new races. Once the sport has appeared its peculiarities can often be fixed and accentuated by selection, but no amount of deliberate selection can cause a sport to appear.

The characters possessed by two distinct strains or races can usually be combined by a second procedure, that of hybridisation or crossing. By this is meant the artificial breeding together of two individuals, each from a different strain, so that the progeny will exhibit a mixture of the characters of both parents. Flower colour may again be used as a simple illustration. A red-flowered individual may be bred with a white-flowered individual so that a series of progeny with intermediate colour, various shades of pink, is produced. Similarly it is possible to hybridise two races, each of which shows a desirable character, so that the offspring have something, at any rate, of the value of each parent. The best-known example of this is an animal one, the mule, which is the product of mating a mare with an ass. The mule (a name applied to hybrids generally but especially to this particular hybrid) combines in certain useful ways the desirable features of both the horse and the ass. A great deal can be done by this kind of breeding but it also has its limitations. It is possible to hybridise only races which are very nearly related and besides this the products of such matings are often sterile and the new strain cannot be perpetuated.

The work of Luther Burbank affords an excellent example of what can and cannot be done by selection and by hybridisation. Burbank was an American horticulturist who carried out plant selection on a large scale over many years. Some of his results, such as the huge Shasta daisies and day-lilies that he produced, were most spectacular and have become of wide reputation, but in other directions he was not so successful because of the difficulty of maintaining the necessary high degree of selection after the improved strains had been placed on the market. He spent many years, for instance, in trying to obtain by these means prickly pears (cacti of the genus *Opuntia*) without spines. Success in this would have been of far-reaching importance in providing succulent fodder easily grown in lands too dry for ordinary crops. He did succeed finally in producing some spineless strains, but these did not maintain their essential character when grown under ordinary conditions. Burbank also produced a number of interesting plant strains by selecting from sports, such as the stoneless plums, but these also have not become established. By means of hybridisation, also, he succeeded in obtaining several novel plants like the plumcot, a cross between the plum and the apricot, and the strawberry-raspberry, hybrid between the strawberry and the raspberry, but these too have failed to fulfil all their first promise, chiefly owing to sterility.

These two methods, selection and hybridisation, were, until the beginning of the present century, the only means known of improving plant and animal races, but in the last thirty years or so a third and far more valuable method has become possible by the discovery of some of the actual laws which govern the inheritance of characters in living things. To the science of such inheritance the name Mendelism is given, after the great investigator Mendel whose work formed the basis of it.

It is impossible to discuss the vast subject of Mendelism here at any proper length, or to give anything but a very crude idea of its importance. Its value, expressed shortly, is that by following out certain well-defined laws and processes it is possible to vary the constitution of a race to a very great extent. It is, in fact, now possible by such means to eliminate many undesirable characters and to add many desirable ones, and races of practically any constitution can now be artificially produced in this way. The value of this cannot be better illustrated than by a particular instance, which has incidentally had a most far-reaching effect on one aspect of food production.

It was said earlier that wheat grown in this country has a very high yield, chiefly because the strains of wheat suitable for growth here have the capacity or character of heavy cropping. Unfortunately this character is normally accompanied by several disadvantageous features. British wheats are liable to attack by certain diseases, and not only this but the nature of their grain is such that the flour does not bake well into bread. As a result of these drawbacks much of the advantage of heavy cropping is lost. To obviate these difficulties Professor (now Sir Rowland) Biffen, of Cambridge, many years ago set on foot experiments towards the production, by artificial breeding, of a race of wheat which would have the good cropping character and which at the same time would be unsusceptible to disease and also be good for baking. The procedure adopted was to interbreed strains which possessed the latter features with those which were heavy yielders and gradually to add to the product, by further breedings, other strains which possessed additional desirable characters. The process was a long and difficult one but success was finally achieved and, about the time of the War, there had been gradually built up a strain of wheat which would not only grow well in this country but which showed also good cropping capacity, immunity to several serious diseases and a valuable flour constitution. There had in fact been made by scientific means a race of wheat combining in itself all the more important characters from the point of view of human utility. When perfected, this wheat was made available for agricultural use generally, and to-day it and its descendants, for improvement is still going on, are widely grown, and have had a markedly beneficial effect on the wheat-growing industry of the country. Moreover, other races of wheat have recently been raised in the same kind of way, and their use is spreading all over the wheat-producing areas of the world.

This one example must suffice to illustrate the extraordinary advances which have been made as a result of research into the problems of plant and animal breeding, but such advances have not been restricted to any one class of crops. Almost every kind of cultivated plant and animal has been improved and their value increased in this way, and the total increase of production resulting from it has been enormous.

In the control and prevention of plant diseases too, scientific investigation has been of the greatest possible value. Some diseases have been completely overcome and the danger of others has been much lessened.

Plant diseases are of three kinds. There are, first, those diseases which result from bad or insufficient nutrition due to unsuitable surroundings or soils: then there are those caused by the attacks of animals, and finally but by no means least, those due to the attacks of small parasitic plants, usually fungi. These last are by far the commonest and most dangerous. Naturally enough sick plants cannot be treated like sick people, and once a disease has obtained a hold it is much more difficult to cure it without killing the patient. Sometimes a cure is possible but more often it is not, and attention has therefore been directed chiefly to prevention. Work in this direction has had the most valuable results. The mode of life of the parasitic fungi and other causative agencies has been studied, and by means of the knowledge so gained it has generally been possible to suggest and put into operation effective preventive measures. In particular, the causes of disease have been studied and the predisposing factors have been removed or reduced, and to-day the losses from plant diseases, although still serious enough, are far less than they used to be, and matters are still rapidly improving. The use of antisepsis is spreading: much more is known of how to keep plants healthy and in a condition to resist attack: dangerous conditions in the environment have been eliminated: and in many other ways the dangers have been lessened. The question of breeding races of crop plants which are immune to disease has also received considerable attention and there are many such races now in cultivation, particularly among potatoes.

Other steps also have been taken to combat plant disease. Just as in human disease isolation and quarantine are among the most important methods of preventing the spread of the trouble, so now the same action is taken with plants. Living plants which are likely to be disease carriers may not be imported into countries where the disease would be especially dangerous. Inspectors are maintained to examine imported plants to ensure that they are free from disease. Susceptible crops are often not allowed to be grown in certain regions where disease is prevalent, in the hope that in the absence of host-plants the parasite will ultimately die out. Finally, legal steps are taken to prevent the spread of disease by thoughtless or deliberately careless action. It is true that these latter are scarcely biological methods of prevention, but they have been made effective as a result of biological research.

Although these pages give only a very short outline of the way in which scientific investigation is helping to lessen the action of factors which tend to limit agricultural production, they are amply sufficient to demonstrate how much is being done to put our supplies of food and other commodities on a surer basis. We have at present to rely on the green plant for our well-being and this state of affairs may persist for a long time. While it does, every scientific advance and every piece of scientific, and especially biological, research must mean a definite improvement in our condition.

Chapter VI

CEREALS AND PULSES

INTRODUCTION

Almost all kinds of plants and all parts of plants are used in some way in human dietetics with the exception of the woody parts of trees and other large plants, but most human vegetable food is of three kinds. First there is the food that consists of the foliage of plants. This we eat chiefly because of the salts and vitamins it contains and not for the bulk of the food that it supplies, and such foliage generally contains a very high proportion of water. The greater part of our proteins, carbohydrates and fats are obtained from two other plant sources—storage organs, and fruits and seeds. The reason for the special value of these parts of the plant as human food is interesting. The plant, as a living organism, has much the same responsibilities, if the word may be used, as the human being. These are first to provide food against a time when food manufacture may be impossible, that is, to make provision for the future, and second to store up food for the young plants which are to come after so that they can be maintained until such time as they are self-supporting. In just the same way human beings endeavour to make provision for the future and to take steps to set their offspring up in the world, or at any rate, to provide for them while they are growing up. The plant does these things by making, during the summer season, considerably more food than it actually needs and storing it up in one, or both, of two ways. If the store is to be used later by the plant itself to tide it over an unproductive period, like the winter, and to initiate new growth in the succeeding spring, it is usually concentrated in some special part of the plant which becomes swollen and filled with accumulated supplies of food.

If the store is to be used by the young plants of the new generation it is normally stored up in the seed. Food storage of this kind has naturally to be done with due regard to space, and so seeds especially, and other storage organs in lesser degree, are filled with a very concentrated mixture of food materials. It is for these stores that man grows the plants as crops. Not only is the actual return of food material from them high but, since that food is designed to meet all the requirements of a living organism, it is a particularly well-balanced and complete mixture of food-stuffs. The various root vegetables are the best examples of plants grown for the food stored in their body, and the cereals are the outstanding instances of the cultivation of plants for the sake of their seeds.

The plant is also faced with one necessity that does not concern human beings. This is the need for ensuring that the seeds which are going to provide the new generation shall be conveniently scattered over a wide area so that they have plenty of soil materials to draw upon, and so that they are not overshadowed by the parent plant. This necessity is met in many ways, one of the commonest and most familiar being the white parachutes of the dandelion, which serve to carry off and scatter the fruits by the agency of wind. Another very common method is to make use of the movement and transport of roving animals. This is done in two ways, either by means of seeds and fruits which will adhere to animals and so be carried by them, or by making the seeds and fruits edible and attractive so that they are readily eaten by animals. The seeds of these edible fruits are able to resist digestion and pass through the body of the animal uninjured and, in the course of this passage, which normally takes some time, they are often carried long distances. Fruits of this kind are usually edible and palatable because of the large amount of sugar that they contain and this, of course, makes them valuable for food. Their value in this way has long been realised—indeed it is possible that wild fruits were the original and primaeval food of man, and they have been cultivated for thousands of years. To-day the fleshy fruits of plants form no small part of human plant food and that part is steadily growing, especially now that many fruits are known to be particularly rich in certain vitamins.

With these preliminary remarks we may go on to a more detailed account of the vegetable foods of the human race, their botanical nature and their sources of supply. Human diets vary greatly in different peoples and in different parts of the world. Some peoples are almost exclusively vegetarian, especially if they live in the tropics, where the fats most easily obtained in animal food have not the same importance in maintaining the temperature of the body. Others, like the Eskimos, of colder regions are almost entirely meat eaters, although they take a certain amount of vegetable food during the short arctic summer. But these are extremes, and the peoples of most of the more highly civilised countries have a mixed diet. The nature of the diet also depends very much on the ease with which the different kinds of food can be obtained. The restriction of diet in some countries, as those of warmer eastern Asia, is to some extent due to the ease with which domestic supplies of rice can be grown.

Primitive tropical peoples are largely fruit eaters because the luxuriant natural vegetation of the tropics easily supplies them with a good amount of such food without much trouble to themselves. Similarly flesh eating, hunting and vast supplies of game go hand-in-hand, as was formerly the case with the North American Indians and the bison. The reason why a very mixed diet is characteristic of highly organised societies is that such societies are more wealthy than others and can therefore command a much wider range of commodities, and one of the chief purposes of wealth is to give access to a larger assortment of goods. Education also leads to the greater exploitation of available sources.

Grasses and Cereals

It is proper to begin a study of plant products with the grasses and their fruits, not only because the foods derived from them support by far the greater part of the world's population to-day, but because they have been instrumental in determining the course of human history. It is noteworthy that certain families of flowering plants are very much more valuable to the human race than others, and the family of the Grasses (Gramineae) is the outstanding example of this. Had there been no grasses, civilisation might indeed have developed, but it would probably have developed differently. The world civilisation is essentially a grassland civilisation.

In very broad terms natural vegetation is of three kinds: forest (in which arboreal plants tend to be present almost exclusively); grassland (where this particular kind of herb forms a complete covering); and desert (where the vegetation consists only of a comparatively few highly specialised plants). There are, of course, very many intermediate conditions, but over much of the world the vegetation is of one of these three kinds.

In the very earliest stages of human development before communities attain any real organisation and coherence the distribution of man bears little relation to that of vegetation, except that he is absent from extreme hot and cold districts and tends rather to favour the tropical forests where nature is most lavish with her gifts. Such a state is still to be seen among such peoples as the natives of the Amazon basin, the Pygmies of the Congo basin and such Malayan aborigines as the Dyaks of Borneo. Sooner or later, however, there comes the necessity, probably owing to increasing numbers, for the practice of agriculture, that is of artificially augmenting the natural harvests. This is difficult in the forests, and even more so in the deserts, with the result that the grasslands become the centres of man's development. It would seem probable that these were first exploited as grazing lands for the support of herds and flocks, and that only later did the idea of growing corn purposely evolve. Be this as it may man became tied to the grasslands and as yet shows no sign of regaining his independence even if he wished to do so. The extraordinary facilities which the grassland regions possess for the rapid establishment and spread of human civilisation is exemplified extremely well by the remarkable speed with which such countries as the Argentine and Uruguay, which, economically, depend chiefly on the enormous areas of grass lands they contain, have developed. Only less striking is the more familiar instance of North America and Canada, with their plains and prairies.

Human history is to a very large extent the story of the conflicts of peoples under the stress of population increase and agricultural stringency, as was seen even in the Great War, for which a contributory cause was the tremendous population pressure in Germany, but this has been greatly intensified during the course of history by change in the distribution of vegetation in the world. The story of the Ice Ages makes us familiar with climatic changes on a great scale and their effect upon the earth, but it is generally not sufficiently realised that, although the intense changes of glaciation have passed away, changes of lesser significance have persisted and are continuing to-day. What these changes have been in detail is a matter so controversial that we must avoid it, but that there have been changes permits of no question. Vegetation is rigidly bound to climate and if there are changes in one there are usually changes in the other, since a climatic change is really an alteration in the position of certain given conditions and vegetation moves in correlation with this alteration. The effect of this has been very great.

It is always difficult to assess the relative values of human events, but if we were asked to say what we consider to have been the event with the most far-reaching effect on human development, we should probably be very nearly correct in answering—the lengthy and extensive migration of peoples outward from the interior of Asia. This in turn is based upon

the fact that central Asia has been becoming, probably ever since the Ice Ages, more and more desiccated and cold. The environment has changed, and of a necessity the inhabitants, both plant and animal, have changed too. What does not change is the relation between mankind and the grassland and, as the latter moves, the former must follow. Much more might be said on this subject but we must confine ourselves to two other rather different examples. Of the civilisations of the past which have left monumental vestiges two at once strike the imagination, those of north Africa (Egyptian and Roman) and tropical America (the Mayas and the Aztecs). Where the former flourished is now little better than desert. Where the latter lived is much dense forest. Both conditions would to-day make human habitation on a large scale impossible. Climate gradually changed, and we may at least suggest that this change helped to sound the knell of these ancient civilisations.

The Gramineae is a large family with over six thousand species, and a very specialised one. Both in vegetative organisation and in floral structure the grasses have many unique characters which fit them for the rôle they play in nature as a whole, and there are no other plants quite, or even very, like them. Economically their value is twofold, their foliage and stems providing food for grazing animals and their fruits providing food for mankind. In both animals and humans they furnish the staple articles of diet.

The name cereal is given to those grasses which provide grain for human consumption. Grain is often referred to as the seed of grasses, but many readers of these pages will know that this is, from a botanical point of view, incorrect and that it is the fruit of these plants, comprising not only the seed but the carpellary structures too. Scientifically the kind of fruit concerned is called a *caryopsis*, which may be defined as a one-seeded indehiscent fruit in which the carpel wall and the seed coat are united, but for general purposes the word grain is sufficiently accurate.

The great value of grain lies in the fact that it contains reserve food (endosperm) in a very concentrated and comparatively dry condition easy to store, grind and bake, and secondly that its constitution is such as to make it specially suitable for human food. The grasses concerned are also annuals and easy to cultivate extensively.

These and other attendant minor advantages have resulted in the grasses becoming the source of the staple food supplies of practically the whole human race with the possible exceptions of a few forest and desert peoples. This being so and taking into consideration also the number of known grass species, it might reasonably be supposed that an enormous number is cultivated in various parts of the world. Actually this is far from being the case and, if tropical regions are excluded, the whole supply of grain is furnished by half-a-dozen cereal crops. These are wheat, oats, barley, rye, rice and maize. These will be dealt with first and, in conclusion, some account will be given of the peculiarly tropical grains which, although they support very large populations, have nothing approaching the same total importance.

Of the cereals wheat takes undisputed pride of place, not only as regards the amount of production but for many other reasons too. Nearly all highly civilised countries use wheat bread as their staple food because wheat flour bakes into a more appetising and wholesome bread than any other flour. But wheat is also a good deal more expensive to produce than other grains and the poorest peoples cannot afford wheat bread. Hence the consumption of wheat in a country has come to be regarded as an indication of that country's general level of culture. Wheat has, in fact, what is called a "prestige value". For the reasons already indicated it is consumed chiefly in the countries of Europe and in North America, but it is also used extensively in other parts of the world, even in eastern Asia, where the dominant food is rice. The great wheat-producing areas of the world are the U.S.A., Russia, Canada, India, France, Argentine, Italy, Australia and Spain. Of these

the first two account for nearly as much as all the rest put together. These countries consume within their own boundaries very different proportions of their harvests, so that some are exporting countries and some are not. Canada is the leading wheat-exporting country, sending out three times as much as the U.S.A., which comes next, and which actually itself consumes seven-eighths of its production. Argentine and Australia are also great exporting countries. France, on the other hand, although a great producer, has also to import a little to provide sufficient for its own people. Notwithstanding the widespread cultivation of wheat there are still many regions capable of exploitation in this way, such as parts of temperate South America and the cooler parts of Africa. Apart from the grain and flour as such several other foods are made from wheat flour. The most important of these are semolina, macaroni and vermicelli.

The history of wheat, which has been cultivated since Neolithic times, is "wrapt in mystery". No wild plant is known to-day which can confidently be said to represent the ancestor of any of the cultivated forms, at any rate the more common ones, but the ancestral plants were presumably natives of western or central Asia. Botanically the wheats of to-day belong to the genus *Triticum*, but there is much diversity of opinions as to their classification within that group. Some consider that three species are involved, others recognise two only, but whichever, if either, is correct, there are certainly many forms of the plant. Common bread wheats such as are grown in this country are generally referred to as *Triticum vulgare*, while *T. durum* and *T. polonicum* are the sources of the flour from which the macaroni products are made. It may also be mentioned as a point of interest that some varieties are "bearded", that is to say, the flowers bear awns, so that they tend to resemble the ordinary barleys.

Barley is the next in importance of the temperate cereals. It requires much the same conditions for cultivation as wheat but can be grown in colder places and, in fact, farther north

than any other grain. Its features are much those of wheat in lesser degree but it cannot compete with that crop for bread making. To-day it is chiefly used as a source of malt, from which beer is made, but its flour is also used for food to a limited extent. In former times its value for this purpose was much greater.

Barley is grown to some extent in nearly all the countries of the northern temperate zone but the chief sources are the U.S.A., Germany and India. It is the most widely distributed cereal and is grown even in parts of the tropics. Pearl barley is the grain after it has been polished. Barley appears to have been derived from the species *Hordeum vulgare* or *H. spontaneum* which still grows wild in western Asia. Three cultivated races are generally recognised, differing in the number of rows of fruits in the ear. Just as in wheat there are bearded and beardless varieties.

The oat is essentially a North American and European cereal, the greatest producing countries being the U.S.A., Canada, Russia, Germany and Poland. Its area of cultivation is much that of barley and it has much the same northern limit —about 70° N. In our own islands it is specially associated with Scotland, where its meal affords an almost national food material. This is highly nutritious, but cannot be baked into bread and so is mostly consumed as porridge. Outside Scotland it is used chiefly as fodder either as the grain or as the green crop.

There is reason to believe that all the cultivated varieties of oats are derived from a prehistoric European and west-Asian species, *Avena sativa*, which in turn is derived from a widely distributed wild plant, *A. fatua*.

Rye is the last of the important temperate cereals and is specially grown where the soil is poor and unsuitable for better crops. It is grown to some degree in nearly all European countries, but Russia is by far the largest producer, with Germany and Poland some distance behind. The black bread familiar in many continental countries is made from rye flour,

but its food value is considerably less than that made from wheat. The crop is also used as green fodder and, to a certain extent, for malt production. Rye is nearly all consumed in the countries where it is grown and even Russia exports only a small amount. The straw of rye like that of most other cereals has a variety of uses. The scientific name of rye is *Secale cereale*, and there are several cultivated forms.

Rice, which is the next cereal to be considered, actually contributes more largely to the dietary of mankind than any other food-stuff, and for this reason and because of the enormous numbers of people who subsist mainly or entirely upon it must rank as the most generally important of plant products. It differs from the cereals hitherto mentioned in requiring very much warmer conditions for its growth, and in the method of its cultivation, which needs a great deal of water. The centre of its production is therefore that part of the world where these conditions prevail—the monsoon region of eastern Asia. The chief producing countries are China, India, Japan, Java, Indo-China and Siam. On a much smaller scale it is often cultivated outside Asia, as in Brazil and Madagascar, and quite an appreciable amount is grown in the Lombardy plain of northern Italy. In spite of this enormous and widespread production very little rice (not more than 10 per cent. of the whole) enters commerce. All the rest is consumed in the lands of production. For wheat the corresponding figure is about one-quarter. The huge populations of India and China consume immense quantities, although it is to be remembered that wheat is also grown in these regions to a considerable extent.

Rice is a valuable food-stuff, but compared with other cereals is deficient in fats and proteins, and a diet mainly of rice has therefore to be supplemented by some proportions of other foods richer in these ingredients. Moreover rice lacks the particular proteins that are of importance in baking and cannot be used for bread. It is eaten boiled or cooked into little cakes. The grain can be fermented to yield an alcoholic drink known as saki or arak. Cultivated races belong to the species *Oryza sativa*. It has been cultivated in numerous forms for thousands of years but is also frequently found wild.

Maize, the last of the major cereals, is the only one with a New World origin, where it has been cultivated for an unknown length of time. In North America, where nearly three-quarters of the whole world crop is grown and where it is commonly used as a vegetable, it is generally called "corn," a word which is applied in the Old World to any cereal. "Indian corn" is yet another name for it and is probably the original English name bestowed upon the plant by those who introduced it to Britain from North America in the sixteenth century.

Maize is a poor bread maker, and in most civilised countries is used chiefly as a poultry and stock food or as a source of certain sugars. It has, however, become an important food material for certain semi-civilised native races, particularly the Bantu tribes of Africa, who to-day subsist largely on the meal it yields. It grows best in warm countries, and patches of "mealies" are a familiar sight in the neighbourhood of native kraals. The plant requires for its cultivation conditions warmer than those of our own country, where it ripens only in favoured spots and in good seasons. It is generally grown throughout the tropics, but North America supplies nearly the whole of the huge amounts that enter commerce.

Until a few years ago nothing was known certainly about the origin of maize, which is called scientifically *Zea Mays*, and there was no wild American grass at all resembling it. Lately, however, it has been definitely established that it is an abnormal form of a fairly well-known wild grass, *Euchlaena mexicana*, which is a native of Mexico.

The minor cereals, which have now to be described, are for the most part tropical species cultivated for local consumption by native peoples untouched by white civilisation. Most of them therefore have, from our point of view, a very limited interest, but a few have gradually become widely dispersed and more important. Their great centre is tropical Africa, with

MAP I

its enormous and complex native population. In Asia the predominance of rice is almost complete and the needs of the small native populations of America have been largely met by maize.

The most important minor cereals are as follows:

Tropical America. *Zizania palustris*, resembling rice, was formerly cultivated by the North American Indians. Teosinte, the plant from which maize is derived, also furnishes a grain. *Bromus Mango* formerly afforded a grain to the native Chilians.

Tropical Asia. A second species of *Zizania*, *Z. latifolia*, gives some grain, but the most important are ragi (*Eleusine coracana*), broom-corn millet (*Panicum miliaceum*), pearl millet (*Pennisetum typhoideum*), and Koda millet (*Paspalum scrobiculatum*). All these originated in India but are now grown throughout the Old World tropics. Soft-fruited varieties of Job's tears (*Coix Lacryma-Jobi*) are also used to some extent.

Tropical Africa. The great native African grains belong to the genus *Sorghum* and the most useful are Guinea corn (*S. guineense*), Kaffir corn (*S. caffrorum*), and durra (*S. Durrha*). Among the less general are two species of *Digitaria* (*D. Iburua* and *D. exilis*), Guinea grass (*Panicum maximum*), two species of *Echinochloa* (*E. pyramidalis* and *E. stagnina*), and the teff (*Eragrostis abyssinica*).

Finally, there are one or two grains which fall into none of these categories. Chief of these are the Italian or fox-tail millet (*Setaria italica*), which is fairly widely grown in the warm temperate Old World, and of familiar use in our own country as a food for cage birds, the cockspur millet (*Echinochloa frumentacea*) from Asia, and the common millet (*Sorghum vulgare*), cultivated in many warm countries.

PULSES

Another family, the Leguminosae, to which belong the peas and beans, affords a series of food products comparable with the cereals and the parallel between the two is, in many ways, close. The actual products are in this case seeds and not fruits, although the pods are sometimes eaten as well. These seeds, like the cereals, contain all the important food substances in well-balanced proportions and they, also, are convenient to store and to prepare for consumption. Here again, too, the plants are mostly annuals and give a good yield with fairly simple cultivation methods. On the whole their chemical constitution is such that they are comparatively rich in proteins and fats, so that they form useful complementary foods to the cereals, and the two are often used in combination. They are, however, generally of more value as fresh vegetables, and are therefore more often cultivated on a small horticultural scale. When used in the fresh condition they are normally consumed where they are cultivated and scarcely enter commerce. Like the cereals they afford many useful green forage crops, including the numerous clovers and lucernes. They have also a general name comparable to the term cereals—they are known as pulses.

As might be expected with such a close resemblance the geographical segregation of the different pulse crops follows in general the lines seen in the cereals. There are certain widely grown temperate kinds, and a larger and more miscellaneous collection of tropical sorts. It is convenient to consider them under these heads.

The Pulses of Temperate Lands

The best known of these are the kinds usually and commonly grown in gardens in England and similarly situated countries. Such are the broad bean (*Vicia Faba*), said to have been introduced into China in 3000 B.C.; the runner bean (*Phaseolus multiflorus*); and the garden pea (*Pisum sativum*). The field bean and the field pea are rather coarse forms of the garden species and are grown usually on an agricultural scale, often for forage. On the continent of Europe the French or haricot bean (*Phaseolus vulgaris*) is an important crop.

The lentil (*Ervum Lens*) is a small kind of pea grown chiefly in the Mediterranean lands and traded in a dry condition. Two or three kinds of lupin (*Lupinus* spp.) are also cultivated, but mostly for forage.

There remains one warm temperate pulse that calls for special comment, the soya or soy bean (*Glycine Soja*). This plant is grown extensively in many parts of the world but especially in China and Manchuria. Its value lies first in the suitability and richness in proteins of its food reserves, which contain four times as much as wheat, and secondly in the large number of ways in which it can be utilised. In China, for example, it is used as a dry food, as a fresh food, as green fodder, for cattle cake, for illuminating oil, as a substitute for lard, as a source of lubricating grease, for the manufacture of a vegetable milk, as a substitute for coffee and in varnishing and lacquering. Even this list does not exhaust its possibilities and there has recently been put on the market a flour, called soy yolk, made from it. In short, from the human point of view the soya bean seems to be the nearest approach to the perfect plant product. Its cultivation and use has increased enormously in the last few decades, and in 1929 the world production amounted to $6\frac{1}{2}$ million tons, of which China and Manchuria contributed 5 millions. In the latter country the soya bean is said to occupy one-quarter of the whole cultivated area. Repeated attempts have been made to produce a strain suitable for growing in our own country, but so far without much success.

The Pulses of Tropical Lands

These are so numerous that it is difficult to know how many to mention, but those cited here certainly represent the most important. They are arranged here according to what are supposed to be their native countries, but some of them have been cultivated so long that it is uncertain whence they came originally and due allowance must be made for this.

In the warmer parts of America the Lima bean (*Phaseolus lunatus*), the tepary bean (*Phaseolus acutifolius*) and the potato bean (*Apios tuberosa*) are frequently grown as vegetable crops. A more markedly tropical species is the jack bean (*Canavalia ensiformis*).

The Old World species are, as might be expected, more numerous, even omitting special mention of several kinds of *Phaseolus* grown in eastern Asia. Among the more notable are the chick pea (*Cicer arietinum*), the pigeon pea (*Cajanus indicus*), the sword bean (*Canavalia gladiata*), the cow pea (*Vigna sinensis*), the pod of which is eaten whole, and the hyacinth bean (*Dolichos Lablab*), which also has an edible pod. Less important are the green and black grams (*Phaseolus Mungo*), the blackeye pea (*Vigna Catjang*), the velvet beans (*Mucuna* or *Stizolobium* spp.), the asparagus bean (*Dolichos sesquipedalis*), the Goa bean (*Psophocarpus tetragonolobus*), and the yam bean (*Pachyrhizus* spp.).

Two tropical pulses deserve special mention not only because of their value but also for a purely botanical reason. These are the earth nut or pea nut (*Arachis hypogaea*) from America, and the bambarra nut (*Voandzeia subterranea*) from Africa. In both the flower stalks bend down into the ground after the flowers have withered and the fruits or pods ripen below the surface. Both furnish most valuable foods and are also important as sources of oil. The latter is less widely known but has great possibilities. It is said that African native messengers can travel almost all day on a handful of the beans. In constitution they resemble the soya bean.

The seeds of three other plants are used in the same way as cereals and pulses but belong to neither of those groups. The first is the buckwheat (*Fagopyrum esculentum*), belonging to the same family as the docks and sorrels. It is chiefly grown in Russia, France and the U.S.A., and is used both for human food, as for instance in buckwheat cakes, and for fodder, especially for chicken food. The others are the quinoa (*Chenopodium Quinoa*) a South American plant, and *Amaranthus caudatus*, a plant grown chiefly in India.

Chapter VII

VEGETABLES: SALAD PLANTS: FRUITS

VEGETABLES

From the pulses, which are used both dry and fresh, it is an easy step to the other plant products which afford fresh material for culinary purposes, that is to say which are normally cooked before consumption. There is no accurate and convenient term for this collection of commodities, but the name "vegetable", popularly applied to them, is quite serviceable. Salad plants and fruits will be discussed later.

Here, even more than before, we are faced with the impossibility of giving anything approaching a complete list of these plants or at least of the tropical sorts, because hundreds are cultivated in different parts of the world and many are scarcely known outside certain small areas. The temperate kinds are not so numerous, and nearly all of them can be mentioned.

Vegetables, since they are cooked fresh and tend often to be delicate in structure, hardly enter commerce as such and their trade is generally purely local, although often considerable. Some are grown as field crops but most come from market gardens. Their intensive and forced cultivation has, of late years, assumed considerable importance and more recently still they have become, in conjunction with fruits, the materials for a great canning industry. The growth of this industry, in Great Britain at any rate, is shown by figures for 1927 and 1931. In the former year 2 million tins of vegetables were produced; in the latter year the number had risen to 56 millions and outweighed the similar treatment of fruits.

Almost every part of the plant is utilised in one or other of the vegetables, although among the commoner kinds the parts of value are those organs in which reserve food is stored, and to classify them on this basis is the most simple way of dividing them into groups. But before this is done one outstanding vegetable, the potato, must be dealt with separately, as its merits warrant.

The Potato

So firmly is the position of the cereals as the premier plant products established that it will probably come as a surprise to most of those who read these pages to hear that in terms of bulk yield the potato is by far the most important of the world's crops. It is worth while to illustrate this statement with some figures. In the year 1925 the production, in millions of tons, of potatoes and the four chief cereals was as follows:

Potatoes	...	185	Rice	...	84
Wheat	...	104	Oats	...	67
Maize	...	96			

In one sense this is apt to be misleading because the cereals give a very concentrated and relatively dry product while in the potato a very large proportion of the tuber is water, and the actual area of cultivation of this crop is less than that of any of the four cereals, but the figures are nevertheless striking.

This enormous yield comes almost entirely from European countries, in the following order (the figures are again in millions of tons):

Russia	...	44	U.S.A.	...	9
Germany	...	41	Czechoslovakia	...	7
Poland	...	29	Great Britain	...	$5\frac{1}{2}$
France	...	15			

It will be seen that, except for Russia, Germany easily leads the list, a fact that was of almost supreme importance to that country during the War. In Great Britain the potato is actually the most important of all arable crops. It is interesting to note also that the potato has a special value in agriculture, in that its cultivation absorbs more labour at a profitable rate than that of any other crop.

The question of the botanical origin of the potato (*Solanum tuberosum*) and the history of its introduction into Europe are very involved matters which cannot be fully discussed here, but some general statements may be made. The plant is derived undoubtedly from a wild species indigenous to South America, but to what part is uncertain. The actual cultivated plant is unknown now in a wild state and, although there are several wild species which resemble it more or less closely and which come from Chile and Uruguay, it is doubtful which, if any, of them is really its ancestor.

Similarly we cannot be sure just how it came to Europe except that it was towards the end of the sixteenth century. The widely accepted story that it was brought to England either by Sir Walter Ralegh or Sir Francis Drake cannot, alas, be substantiated and it was probably due to some much less exalted personage, and perhaps to Ralegh's companion, Thomas Herriott. It would appear also that it was in fact twice introduced into Europe, once to Spain and once to England.

The portion of the plant used commercially is the swollen and tuberous underground stems in which reserve food is stored. The composition of these tubers is usually about 80 per cent. water, 16 per cent. starch and 2 per cent. protein. The plant contains a poisonous glucoside, solanin, normally present in the tubers in such small amount as to be harmless, but if they are allowed to become green by exposure to light the amount is sometimes injurious.

The potato is valuable not only as food but also as a source of alcohol, starches, dextrine and glucose.

Other Stem-tuber Vegetables

Besides the potato the only familiar temperate plant bearing stem tubers is the Jerusalem artichoke (*Helianthus tuberosus*). This plant is a close relation of the sunflower of gardens and,

like it, is a native of North America. The name "Jerusalem" is a corruption of the French word "girasol".

Among tropical plants the yams are the best known stem-tuber vegetables. They belong to the genus *Dioscorea*, and many of them also have root tubers. They are important foods for native races but are rarely seen in temperate lands.

Root Vegetables

These are very numerous and fall into two groups, a smaller one in which root tubers are produced and a larger one in which the main tap roots are swollen with reserve food. To the first belong the Chinese artichoke (*Stachys Sieboldii*) and the sweet potato (*Ipomoea Batatas*). In some warm countries, as in the southern States of North America, the latter rivals the true potato in popularity.

The members of the second group are among the most important and familiar vegetables and are mostly natives of Europe. The turnip (*Brassica campestris*) and the rutabaga (*Brassica campestris* var.) are valuable both for food and fodder, as is also the swede (*Brassica campestris* var.), together with the beet (*Beta vulgaris*) and its variety the mangold wurzel. The sugar beet, considered more fully elsewhere, is also sometimes eaten. Next come the carrot (*Daucus Carota*) and the parsnip (*Pastinaca sativa*). The radish (*Raphanus sativus*) is, in effect, a small edition of the turnip, but the rather similarly named horse-radish (*Armoracia rusticana*) is quite a distinct plant with long tough roots, chiefly used for flavouring.

Less well known, and with a much more restricted use, are chervil (*Chaerophyllum bulbosum*), skirret (*Sium Sisarum*), salsify (*Tragopogon porrifolius*), scorzonera (*Scorzonera hispanica*), and scolymus (*Scolymus hispanica*). Celeriac is a form of celery (*Apium graveolens*) in which the root is swollen like a turnip. It is of recent development and has not yet attained any great popularity.

Of tropical root vegetables the numerous yams have already been mentioned.

Leaf Vegetables

Chief among these are the cabbage (*Brassica oleracea*), a native of Europe, including the British Isles, and its varieties Brussels sprouts (*B. oleracea* var. *gemmifera*), kale (*B. oleracea* var. *acephala*) and kohl-rabi (*B. oleracea* var. *caulorapa*). Cabbage in one or other of its forms is said to have been cultivated since 2500 B.C. The Chinese cabbage (*B. pekinensis*) is sometimes grown in America and elsewhere.

Spinach (*Spinacia oleracea*), an Asiatic plant, is a favourite vegetable, and a similar plant, the New Zealand spinach (*Tetragonia expansa*) is sometimes grown. Orache (*Atriplex hortensis*) and chard (*Beta vulgaris* var. *cicla*) are less common. The mustards (*Brassica alba* and *B. nigra*) are also occasionally used.

Stem Vegetables

The only notable member of this group is the asparagus (*Asparagus officinalis*), European, in which the whole young shoot is eaten. Certain other plants are sometimes substituted for the true asparagus.

Leaf-base Vegetables

In these it is the petioles and leaf bases which, usually blanched, are eaten. Celery (*Apium graveolens*) is one of the most familiar, while sea-kale (*Crambe maritima*) is less frequently seen. These are both European species. Strictly speaking the leek (*Allium Porrum*), Asiatic, must be included here, although it links on to the bulb vegetables mentioned below. In the rhubarb (*Rheum rhaponticum*) from northern Asia, the petioles have a sweet flavour and are generally used without much blanching. The leaf blades of this plant are dangerous because of the large amount of oxalic acid they contain.

Bulb Vegetables

These all belong to the genus *Allium* and are natives of Europe and west Asia. The onion (*A. Cepa*) of very longstanding cultivation is the commonest, although the shallot (*A. asca-lonicum*) is often grown. The garlic (*A. sativum*), the chipple (*A. fistulosum*) and the chive (*A. Schoenoprasum*) are used chiefly for flavouring.

Inflorescence Vegetables

In three well-known vegetables it is the inflorescence, or por-tions of it, that is eaten. The globe artichoke (*Cynara Scolymus*), a native of the Mediterranean countries, is a large thistle-like herb, and the edible part consists of the outer bracts of the capitulum. In the cauliflower and the broccoli (*Brassica oleracea* var. *botrytis*) the inflorescences have, by cultivation, become fleshy when in bud. The difference between these two is merely that the former matures earlier in the year.

SALAD PLANTS

These do not strictly fall within our definition of vegetables because they are eaten uncooked, but we may conveniently deal with them here because they lead on to the next subject. Those in general use in Europe are all natives of that continent.

By far the most important is the lettuce (*Lactuca sativa*), which may be compared to a small uncooked cabbage, al-though it is not related, botanically, to that plant. Cos lettuce is a form with longer, more rigid, leaves.

Endive (*Cichorium Endivia*) and chicory (*C. Intybus*) re-semble lettuce in appearance and use, but the latter is also grown for its root, which when finely ground affords a sub-stitute and adulterant for coffee. In corn salad (*Valerianella olitoria*) and watercress (*Nasturtium officinale*) also, the leaves are eaten, and in the dandelion (*Taraxacum Dens-leonis*) both leaves and root. The foliage of parsley (*Petroselinum hortense*) is mostly used for garnishing. In mustard (*Brassica alba*) and cress (*Lepidium sativum*) it is the seed-leaves (epigeal cotyledons) which are edible.

Besides these, many other plants growing in a wild state can be used for salads, and are so employed in country districts. Many of the previously mentioned vegetables, too, can be used uncooked in salads. There is, for instance, a small purple variety of the potato grown for this purpose.

FRUITS

The term "fruit" is used here in a popular and not in a scientific way, to comprise those plant commodities which are generally described as dessert or salad fruits. On the one hand it obviously does not include all commercial carpellary structures, since cereals and many pulses are of this nature, but on the other hand it does include certain items which are not actually formed of ripened carpels. The question of the exact morphological nature of the different commercial "fruits" is a very interesting one and appropriate references will be made to it. Meanwhile it may be said here that fruits are of three kinds: multiple, when several flowers combine to give a single ripened structure; aggregate, when the fruit of a single flower is composed of a number of distinct and separate carpels; and simple fruits, when the flower develops into one single and undivided fruit. The last sort, which is much the commonest, can be classified further into true fruits, where the product is composed of carpellary structures only, and false fruits, which are composed of carpels together with some other organ or organs. The commonest false fruits are the products of flowers with inferior ovaries where the receptacle or top of the flower stalk normally ripens with the carpels. Very occasionally the application of the word "fruit" is a complete misnomer.

For our present purpose it is convenient to classify fruits geographically and to recognise three classes, those of temperate lands, those from the warm temperate zones, and tropical kinds. The last group is actually the largest, but most of the species in it are of such local value that they cannot be mentioned here and only the most general sorts will be noticed.

The Fruits of Temperate Lands

The species of two genera belonging to the family Rosaceae afford most of the really important temperate fruits. To the genus *Prunus* belong the plums (*P. communis* vars.), the almond (*P. Amygdalus*), the peach (*P. Persica*), with its smooth-skinned variety the nectarine (var. *nucipersica*), the apricot (*P. Armeniaca*) and the cherries, of which there are broadly speaking two kinds, the sweet (*P. avium*) and the bitter (*P. Cerasus*). To the genus *Pyrus* belong the apples (*Pyrus Malus*) and the pears (*P. communis*), while two very closely related genera contain the medlar (*Mespilus germanica*) and the quince (*Cydonia vulgaris*). The last is too acid to be eaten raw but makes an admirable conserve. The same remark applies also to certain species of *Pyrus*, like the service (*P. Sorbus*) and the mountain ash or rowan (*P. Aucuparia*). The *Pyrus* fruits are false fruits, the fleshy part being composed chiefly of receptacle tissue; the *Prunus* fruits, on the other hand, are true fruits. All the species mentioned are natives of Europe and western Asia.

The family Rosaceae also includes the brambles, raspberries and strawberries, of which the two first belong to the genus *Rubus*. These fruits are aggregate fruits, being composed of a number of separate small drupelets. The best known species in cultivation are the raspberry (*R. Idaeus*) and the blackberry (*R. fruticosus*), but there is a whole host of other species and varieties, many of them obtained by hybridisation. Details of them can best be sought in fruit-tree catalogues and the only one worth mention here is the loganberry (*R. Loganobaccus*). There is some doubt as to what this plant really is, but many authorities regard it as a cross between a bramble and a raspberry. The strawberry (*Fragaria vesca*) is an aggregate fruit too—the little pips are achenes—but it is also a false fruit since the edible part is entirely composed of the swollen and succulent receptacle. The genera *Rubus* and *Fragaria* are widespread, but the species mentioned above are all European.

Next in importance come the gooseberry (*Ribes Grossularia*), the red currant (*R. rubrum*) and the black currant (*R. nigrum*), also natives of Europe. All three occur apparently wild in our own country but are perhaps actually escapes from cultivation. These fruits, with the raspberries, blackberries and strawberries, are generally spoken of as the "soft" fruits. They are too fleshy to keep long in a fresh state but are nowadays canned in great quantities.

Small but palatable fruits are afforded by several species of the genus *Vaccinium*. The cranberry (*V. Oxycoccus*) and the whortleberry or bilberry (*V. Myrtillus*) are natives of Eurasia, while the large cranberry (*V. macrocarpum*) and the blueberry (*V. corymbosum* and other spp.) are natives of North America. Cranberries keep and travel fairly well and supplies imported from continental countries, especially Russia, are familiar in fruiterers shops.

The mulberry (*Morus alba* and *M. nigra*) ripens in favourable parts of our country, although it is a native of rather warmer parts of the Old World. It is a multiple fruit consisting of the carpels and fleshy perianth leaves of a complete inflorescence. Mulberries are highly esteemed as a delicacy but the trees are widely grown in Asia for their foliage, which is the food of the silkworm.

The tomato (*Solanum Lycopersicum*) and the egg plant or aubergine (*S. Melongena*) are instances of fruits which are chiefly used in salads. The former is a native of America, the latter of Asia.

Walnuts, cobnuts and filberts are the dry indehiscent fruits of *Juglans regia*, *Corylus avellana* and *C. maxima* respectively. All three are natives of Europe and western Asia.

The Fruits of Warm-temperate Lands

There are two competitors for first place among the warm temperate fruits, oranges and grapes. Regarding them simply as edible fruits the former must certainly be considered the winner.

The oranges and their close relations belong to the genus *Citrus* and all are presumably natives of tropical or warm Asia, although many of them have been cultivated so long that they are no longer known in a wild state. Their classification and naming, too, is very confused, but the following is a common way of arranging the different kinds. The true oranges belong to the species *Citrus Aurantium*, of which there are three varieties—the Seville or bitter orange, used for marmalade making (*C. Aurantium* var. *amara*), the sweet or China orange (*C. Aurantium* var. *sinensis*), and the bergamot (*C. Aurantium* var. *Bergamia*). The species *Citrus Medica* also includes three important varieties, namely the lemon (*C. Medica* var. *Limonum*), the lime (*C. Medica* var. *acida*), from which lime-juice is made, and the sweet lime (*C. Medica* var. *Limetta*). The mandarin or tangerine oranges are forms of the species *C. nobilis*. *C. Paradisi* is the grape fruit and a very similar species *C. grandis* is the shaddock or pomelo. The kumquat (*C. japonica*) is the smallest of the group and is used chiefly for preserving. All the species are of the greatest importance, not only for their flavour but also for their nutritional qualities, and the great increase in their consumption is one of the most notable recent developments in human dietetics. Besides those mentioned already there are many minor forms and hybrids. The "blood" orange, for instance, is a variety of the common orange which originated some time ago in Malta. In addition to their use as whole fruits the making of drinks from their juice is now a considerable industry.

The grapes are not only extremely valuable as food but also as a source of wine (see below). All the kinds commonly grown for both purposes belong to the species *Vitis vinifera*, originally a native of western Asia, but two American species *V. aestivalis*, the summer grape, and *V. Labrusca*, the fox grape, are now frequently cultivated, as they are more resistant than the older species to certain diseases and insect pests. There are both black and white varieties of *V. vinifera*, the latter being called muscats. Great quantities of grapes enter commerce in a semi-dry condition in which they will keep for long periods. The most important forms of these products are the raisin, the sultana and the currant. The last named has nothing to do with the red or black currants but is a variety of the grape from Corinth, of which word its English name is a corruption.

Green figs and Turkey figs come from two species of the genus *Ficus*, *F. Carica* and *F. Sycomorus*. Their appreciation is something of an acquired taste and to botanists at any rate they are chiefly of interest morphologically. The so-called "fruit" is a multiple false fruit of a very peculiar kind. The succulent part is the swollen peduncle or inflorescence stalk, the hollow centre of which is lined with innumerable tiny flowers, each producing a small pip-like fruit. The interior of the whole structure communicates with the outside by a small aperture at the thicker end. The genus *Ficus* is very large and many other species are more or less edible. The two mentioned are natives of the Mediterranean countries.

An important series of warm temperate fruits is furnished by members of the Gourd family (Cucurbitaceae). All are false fruits, and some are actually tropical, but they may all be dealt with together here. The pumpkin and its variety, the vegetable-marrow, belong to the species *Cucurbita Pepo*, and the squash (*C. maxima*) and the cushaw pumpkin (*C. moschata*) are close relations. The melon (*Cucumis Melo*) has several varieties, including the netted melon and the Spanish melon, while the cucumber (*Cucumis sativa*) and the gherkin (*C. Anguria*), which is used for pickling, are other members of the same genus. The water melon (*Citrullus vulgaris*) is not to be confused with the true melons, from which it differs in its greater size, black seeds, and pink, more watery, flesh. Rarer members of the family are the chayote (*Sechium edule*) and the calabash cucumber (*Lagenaria vulgaris*). The native countries of these various plants are for the most part uncertain but some are Asiatic and some are American.

The pomegranate (*Punica Granatum*) of the Mediterranean

is another false fruit, peculiar for the two-layered arrangement of the carpel. The fruit has a considerable sentimental reputation, but, at any rate as sold in Britain, is a disappointment when eaten.

The Japanese persimmon (*Diospyros Kaki*) is sometimes seen in our shops. It resembles in size and shape a deep yellow tomato. For some reason it is usually sold in a quite unripe condition, when it is a most astringent and thoroughly unpleasant eatable. The Virginian date plum (*D. virginiana*) from North America, and the common date plum (*D. Lotus*) from western Asia, are smaller-fruited species.

The date (*Phoenix dactylifera*) is a very valuable monocotyledonous fruit grown chiefly in the countries bordering the southern side of the Mediterranean. There it is a most important food and large supplies are also exported.

Although natives of tropical countries, chiefly in America, the various passion fruits may be included here since they are mostly grown in rather cooler lands. The best of them are the passion fruit itself (*Passiflora edulis*) and the granadilla (*P. quadrangularis*). Two other popular species are the water lemon (*P. lancifolia*) and the sweet calabash (*P. maliformis*).

The sweet chestnut (*Castanea sativa*), a native of southern Europe, is an instance of a so-called fruit that is actually a seed. It resembles, but is not related to, the horse chestnut.

In conclusion three comparatively little known fruits may be cited as examples of many others. The first is the Hottentot fig (*Mesembryanthemum edule* and other spp.) from South Africa. The lowquat (*Eriobotrya japonica*) is a native of Asia and has small apple-like fruits. The pistachio nut (*Pistacia vera*) comes from the Mediterranean region.

The Fruits of Tropical Lands

The very few tropical fruits which are familiar commodities give a very false impression of the wealth of hot countries in palatable and edible fruits. The fact that so few of them are known in cooler lands is almost entirely due to the fact that

MAP 2

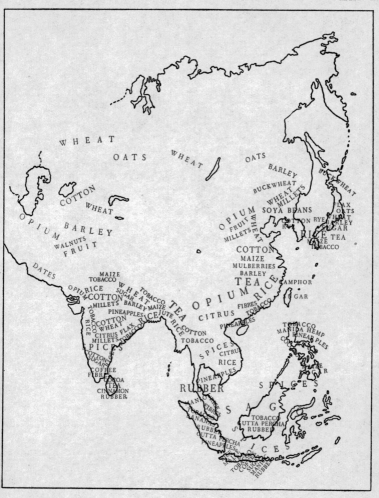

ASIA

the more desirable kinds will not travel well and therefore are consumed only near their place of origin. It is rarely economical to reproduce, even on a small scale, in temperate regions, the conditions necessary for their growth. Within the tropics nearly every country has its characteristic species and the total number eaten somewhere or other is very large. They cannot all be described here and we must confine ourselves to the more ordinary kinds.

Actually there are only four common commercial tropical fruits and these are all very unlike one another. First and foremost are the bananas. Generally speaking there are two forms in cultivation, a larger one properly called the plantain (*Musa paradisiaca*) and a smaller one the true banana (*M. paradisiaca* var. *sapientum*). They are natives of the Old World but are now grown almost all over the tropics, our own supplies coming chiefly from the West Indies. Botanically the banana has several interesting features. It gives a very high yield in cultivation, exceeding, area for area, even the potato. It is one of the few simple fruits containing a considerable quantity of starch. Through long cultivation most races have entirely lost the power of seed production and are propagated solely from the rhizomes. It is now consumed in most temperate countries in far greater quantities than any other tropical fruit, and this is due to the care with which its sea transport has been studied and organised. The popularity of the banana in our own country is of very recent date; the fruit is usually eaten raw but is also excellent cooked as a vegetable; its pulp can be dried into meal, and in some places an alcoholic drink is made from it.

Next in importance to the banana comes the pineapple (*Ananas sativus*), which also is familiar in most temperate countries. It is especially suitable for canning, and great supplies are employed in this way. As a fresh fruit in England it is still rather a delicacy, although second-quality fruits are now imported in considerable quantity. The finest fruits available at home, however, are those grown in glasshouses. The plant is very widely cultivated in nearly all parts of the tropics, but is a native of warm America.

There is a good deal of misunderstanding as to what the pineapple fruit is and how it is borne on the parent plant, and the question "How does a pineapple grow?" is sure to be put sooner or later to anybody who professes a knowledge of botany. The plant itself consists, above ground, of a rosette of long, stiff, narrow, pointed leaves some two or three feet long, from the centre of which a stem of a few feet rises. The "pine-apple" is borne on the top of this stem and the bunch of small leaves at its tip represents the apex of the stem, which if left will go on growing in length. The morphology of the "fruit" itself is also remarkable. The sessile flowers are borne all round the upper part of the stem and, as the carpels ripen, they and the stem fuse together and the whole mass becomes sweet and succulent. The result is thus a multiple false fruit in which stem, bracts and carpels all play a part. In most kinds the seeds do not develop.

A very different looking fruit is the coconut (*Cocos nucifera*). Actually the structure usually sold under this name is not the complete fruit but the seed and inner part of the carpel. The white flesh is the endosperm of the seed, the shell is the endocarp and the whole is a modification of three carpels, of which only one ripens. When growing on the parent tree there is a thick outer fibrous husk formed from the outer parts of the carpels, but this is generally removed before the fruits are transported. In the last few years however the entire fruits have become much more familiar than they used to be because they make excellent nesting shelters for tits and other small birds. The coconut is grown practically everywhere in the tropics, not only for its fruits but also for the hundred and one other uses to which the various parts of it can be put, for to many tropical races it provides almost every requirement. It is probably a native of the Old World.

The only other tropical "fruit" commonly sold in Europe is morphologically a seed—the Brazil nut (*Bertholletia excelsa*).

The hard-shelled nuts are borne by the tree in large spherical woody fruits. The sapucaia nut, the seed of a related plant belonging to the genus *Lecythis*, is also sometimes sold.

Several tropical fruits would certainly be of great commercial value if the difficulty of marketing them fresh could be overcome. Especially is this true of the mango (*Mangifera indica*) from Asia, which has a great reputation for flavour and is occasionally imported. Others are the papaw (*Carica Papaya*), a melon-like fruit; the mangosteen (*Garcinia mangostana*) from Asia; the avocado or alligator pear (*Persea americana*); the guava (*Psidium Guajava*) from Asia; and the sapodilla (*Achras Sapota*) from the West Indies.

The genus *Annona* affords several pleasant fruits occasionally to be seen in our more expensive fruit shops. These include the cherimoyer (*A. Cherimolia*), the sour sop (*A. muricata*), the sweet sop (*A. squamosa*), and the bullock's heart (*A. reticulata*). These are aggregate fruits made up of a number of fleshy carpels. The Cape gooseberry (*Physalis peruviana*) makes a good preserve, and the chillies and red peppers (*Capsicum* spp.), also natives of America, are used as pickles.

Of the less familiar fruits only a selection can be given. The common prickly-pear cacti (*Opuntia* spp.) bear small fruits which are palatable after removal of the small prickles with which they are covered. The ceriman (*Monstera deliciosa*), a multiple fruit looking rather like a short rough cucumber, is sometimes seen in hot-houses. The roselle (*Hibiscus Sabdariffa*) is esteemed for its sweet and fleshy calyces and bracts. The cashew nut (*Anacardium occidentale*) has a remarkable structure; the upper part of the pedicel becomes fleshy and pear-shaped and bears at its tip a kidney-shaped nut which is the real fruit. Still others are the rambutan (*Nephelium lappaceum*), the litchi (*Litchi chinensis*), the jujube (*Zizyphus Jujuba*), the tamarind (*Tamarindus indica*), the rose apple (*Eugenia Jambos*), the bael fruit (*Aegle Marmelos*), the Otaheite apple (*Spondias dulcis*) and the myrobalan (*Terminalia Chebula*). All these are Asiatic. In the New World are the fijoa (*Feijoa

Sellowiana), the star apple (*Chrysophyllum Cainito*) and the mammee apple (*Mammea americana*).

Lastly there are two multiple fruits which, although rarely sold commercially, are of great value to many native communities. These are the bread-fruit (*Artocarpus incisa*) and the jack-fruit (*Artocarpus integrifolia*). Both are natives of Asia and Polynesia and both contain abundant starch. The bread-fruit was once indirectly the cause of an exciting and strange historic episode. It had been known in its native haunts for some little time and it was thought that it might do well if introduced into the West Indies. Accordingly a British man-o'-war, the *Bounty*, was sent, in 1787, to collect a cargo of trees and seeds and carry them to America. Shortly after leaving Tahiti the crew mutinied and cast the commander and his loyal companions adrift in a small boat. This party after great adventures succeeded in reaching Timor. The mutineers meanwhile returned to Tahiti and several of them settled there. Others, fearing capture, sailed, together with a number of native men and women, to an uninhabited island called Pitcairn Island. There they remained unsuspected for twenty years and established a considerable colony which, despite attempts at removal, has persisted there ever since.

Chapter VIII

BEVERAGES: SUGAR AND STARCH: OILS AND FATS: SPICES

TEA, COFFEE AND COCOA

Before the great age of exploration, while much of the world was still unknown, the diets of European peoples were far less varied than they are to-day. Meat, from home-reared stock, filled a much larger place, and beer was almost the only kind of flavoured drink in common use. At that time people were obliged to be content with what they could themselves produce and international trade in food was very small, but as the discovery of new countries and trade routes developed, almost every year saw the addition of some important commodity from overseas. From the point of view of our own country the greatest changes took place in the sixteenth and seventeenth centuries, and in no case were they more far-reaching than in the introduction of the three great beverages—tea, coffee and cocoa. Curiously enough all three came into prominence and popularity about the same time, round 1650, and each of three great divisions of the world, Asia, Africa and America, contributed one of them. It is a striking commentary on the state of world communication up till then that they had all been cultivated and enjoyed in their native countries for many centuries.

Tea is composed of the young leaves and shoots of the Chinese tea plant (*Thea sinensis*), a native of tropical eastern Asia. The plant generally grows as a small bush and the preparation of the commercial product consists of picking the young leaves and buds, rolling them, fermenting them, and finally drying them. Botanically, three varieties of the species *T. sinensis* are recognised, i.e. var. *assamica*, var. *Bohea* and var. *viridis*, but the differences in the finished commodity bear little relation to this classification. Generally speaking tea is either black or green and the distinction lies in the more complete fermentation (oxidation) of the former.

Until a hundred years or so ago tea was almost entirely grown in China, but since then the industry has spread to Burma, India, Ceylon and Java, and these are now the chief producing countries. Minor differences in the methods of preparation and the use of different strains of the plant are largely responsible for the differences in flavour among the commercial brands, well exemplified by "China" and "Indian" tea, but the important chemical ingredients are the same throughout. These are a flavouring oil, the alkaloid caffeine and tannin. The first gives the taste, the second the slightly stimulating effect and the third the colour and strength.

Tea has become almost a national drink in Great Britain, but we do not usually treat it with the respect it deserves. To appreciate its delicate flavour to the full it should be made with great care and drunk without any such additions as milk or sugar.

Two other tea-like beverages have an important local value but do not enter commerce to any extent. Maté or Paraguayan tea consists of the dried and powdered leaves of the South American plant, *Ilex paraguensis*. The drink is made by infusion as in ordinary tea but the leaves are not previously fermented. Khat or Arabian tea is made from the leaves of the shrub, *Catha edulis*.

Coffee is the African contribution to our beverages. The two species from which it is chiefly obtained, *Coffea liberica* and *Coffea arabica*, are natives of eastern tropical Africa, but the ancestral home of the drink is Arabia. The coffee plant is a large shrub with bunches of small white flowers and the "beans", from which the coffee is obtained by roasting and grinding, are the seeds of the red drupaceous fruits. Each drupe contains two seeds and they are covered with a parchment-like endocarp. There are many grades of the product and the choicest is Mocha coffee. Besides its flavour, coffee contains considerable proportions of caffeine and is therefore a valuable stimulant.

The greatest coffee-producing country to-day is Brazil, where there has recently been great over-production. Previously the main supply came from Java and there was also a large industry in Ceylon, but this was devastated about the year 1880 by the attacks of a fungous disease and tea has taken its place.

Cocoa and chocolate are the products of several American trees belonging to the genus *Theobroma*, especially *T. Cacao*. The generic name means the "drink of the gods" and in olden days cocoa, or rather chocolate, was the divine drink of the Aztecs. Cocoa and chocolate are really two names for the same product, obtained by grinding and roasting the seeds or "beans" of the fruits. The cocoa "nibs" so prepared contain a good deal of a fat known as cocoa butter. This has a use in medicine and in certain other directions but tends to be rather unpalatable, and in proprietary brands of cocoa it is generally removed. This kind of cocoa is called soluble cocoa as opposed to what we generally know as chocolate.

The countries from which cocoa chiefly comes to-day are tropical America, the West Indies and western tropical Africa. It is also grown to some extent in Java and Sumatra. Cocoa or cacao, to give it its original name, must not of course be confused with the coconut, a mistake which Dr Johnson made in his *Dictionary*.

A plant called guarana (*Paullinia sorbilis*) provides a similar product in South America and kola nuts from the African tree, *Cola acuminata*, are employed for a similar purpose in that country.

SUGAR

All the food-stuffs so far described are actual parts of plants such as fruits, leaves and stems and are eaten more or less directly and recognisably as such. We have now to consider certain foods which, while of plant origin, are prepared from plants by various methods which leave in them no structural trace of their origin. Foremost among these are sugar and starch.

It was seen in an earlier chapter how important a part is played by the carbohydrates in the life of the plant and particularly by the two types of carbohydrates just mentioned. The value of quite a number of the food-stuffs already alluded to depends upon the presence of these substances, and an appreciable amount of them is absorbed when these foods are eaten. Sugar, however, and to a lesser degree starch, is often required in a separated condition and in greater concentration than occurs naturally in plants, and special methods and processes are adopted to obtain them.

Remembering the high place that sugar occupies among human foods and its wide distribution in plants, it is a little surprising that the whole of our commercial supplies comes from three plants and all but a very small amount from two of these. They are the sugar cane, the sugar beet and the sugar maple.

The sugar cane (*Saccharum officinarum*) is a large tropical member of the grass family and the sugar (cane sugar or saccharose) is obtained by expressing and boiling down the juice of the stems. The sugar cane is, as far as can be ascertained now, a native of Asia, but it has been widely cultivated for many centuries and was introduced into the New World as early as 1500. It is now grown to some extent in nearly all tropical countries, but the chief producers are Cuba, India, Java, Hawaii and Brazil, in the order named. Formosa, Japan, the Philippines, Australia, Porto Rico and Mauritius also supply a considerable amount.

The sugar consumption of the human race has long shown a continual increase. In mediaeval times it was a scarce commodity and replaced as far as possible by honey, but the introduction of tea, coffee and cocoa into Europe was a development which greatly increased the demand. That the increase has continued right up to the present is shown by the fact that the world consumption has risen from 10 to 24 million tons annually in the last thirty years.

It was partly this gradual increase in demand which led to the cultivation of the sugar beet as an additional source of supply, but the most important impetus to this branch of the industry was given by the European blockades associated with the long series of Napoleonic wars. At that time the tropical product could hardly be obtained and attention was turned to the sugar beet, which had been long known as a potential source of supply. Since Napoleonic times the sugar from the sugar cane has become more and more inadequate for world needs, and the growth of sugar beet and the manufacture of the sugar from it is now a large and important industry.

The sugar is extracted from the swollen tap-root of the sugar beet (*Beta vulgaris* var.), in which there is sometimes as much as 17 per cent. of sugar by weight. The product is saccharose as it is in the sugar cane, and the terms cane sugar and beet sugar indicate merely a difference of origin and not a chemical difference. The distribution of sugar beet cultivation is complementary to that of the cane as the plant is a native of temperate regions and it is actually centred almost exclusively in Europe (except for a little in the U.S.A.), where by reason of distance the supply of cane sugar is most precarious. Germany is easily the largest producer, followed by Czechoslovakia, Rumania, France and Poland in that order.

Of recent years great efforts have been made to establish the growth of sugar beet in Great Britain and, with the aid of Government subsidies and guaranteed markets, considerable progress has been made. The industry is centred in East Anglia but small amounts are grown in many parts. History repeated itself in the Great War, when the German submarine campaign unpleasantly emphasised the dangers of relying solely on overseas supplies and thereby gave the necessary initial impetus to beet cultivation in this country.

To-day, the home industry receives a great deal of attention: some think more than it deserves, and it is interesting to give some figures about it. Great Britain consumes annually about $1\frac{1}{2}$ million tons of sugar. The home supply under artificially favourable economic conditions provides about one-ninth of this, and it is unlikely that this could be very much increased without considerable dislocation in other branches of agriculture. It would appear therefore at present that we can never hope to be entirely or even predominantly independent of imported supplies.

It should also be remembered that taking the whole world into consideration, the production of sugar from the cane is still twice as much as that from the beet.

In North America, where maples are among the most abundant trees, an appreciable amount of sugar is obtained from the sap of certain species and especially from the sugar maple (*Acer saccharinum*). The lower part of the trunk of the tree is slashed, usually in spring when the sap is running strongly, and the escaping juice is collected and boiled down. The finished product is usually a thick treacle-like syrup. The supply is limited, and maple sugar is more a delicacy than anything else, although it has a considerable local use. It is worth remarking that it has one advantage over the other two kinds of sugar, in that it can be collected periodically without seriously injuring the plants affording it.

These three plants are the source of all the sugar that enters commerce, but in many parts of the tropics a little is obtained locally from other plants. Many palms, especially those of the genera *Borassus*, *Caryota*, *Cocos* and *Arenga*, provide a sugary juice called toddy, and from it a sugar called jaggery can be extracted. This is chiefly used in the manufacture of alcoholic drinks (see below).

Sugar is sold in many forms. White sugars are the most highly purified kinds, brown sugars are less so, and molasses is the uncrystallizable residue after the remainder has been extracted. From the last named rum is made by fermentation and distillation.

Rather similar but generally more resinous sugary exudations can be obtained from several plants and are usually called "mannas". The commonest come from two species of ash (*Fraxinus Ornus* and *F. rotundifolia*), both from southern Europe, and their secretion is induced by incising the bark. In a number of other plants insect bites fulfil the same purpose. Among these are *Tamarix gallica* and *Alhagi maurorum*, both from the Orient. The Biblical manna was perhaps derived from the former.

STARCH

Starch is distributed in plants in much the same way as sugar, and many common vegetable foods contain it in large proportion, so that most of what is required is absorbed with these foods. Definite starchy foods are, however, prepared from several plants and are more or less important. The chief of these are tapioca, sago and arrowroot, all of which are prepared from the starchy contents of stems and roots.

Tapioca comes from the fleshy root of the manioc (*Manihot utilissima*). The familiar pellets are obtained by expressing and heating the juice in a particular way. This heating is an essential part of the process as the juice is otherwise poisonous. A starch called cassava is also obtained from the same source. The manioc is a native of tropical America but is extensively grown in many parts of the tropics. The commercial tapioca comes chiefly from Malaya.

Sago is prepared from the soft inner portion of the trunks of several kinds of palms, especially members of the genera *Metroxylon* and *Sagus*, natives of tropical Asia. It is similar to tapioca in appearance and use but is generally finer and now, at any rate, less common. The name sago palm is also applied to certain Gymnosperms (*Cycas* spp.) whose seeds yield a kind of sago, but the name is really a misnomer as these plants are in no way related to the true palms.

The name arrowroot, which is a corruption of the native word *aruruta*, is given to similar products from the roots and rhizomes of several distinct plants. West-Indian arrowroot comes from a tropical herb, *Maranta arundinacea*, of tropical America. East-Indian arrowroot is a corresponding product from the root tubers of an Asiatic plant, *Curcuma angustifolia*. Tahiti arrowroot is from the roots of *Tacca pinnatifida*, and Brazilian arrowroot is from the tapioca plant, *Manihot utilissima*.

Besides food supplies much starch is also employed in laundry and other work. This commercial starch can be obtained from many plants rich in this particular kind of carbohydrate and the cereals, except perhaps oats, are particularly often used. Supplies come also from the potato, the buckwheat and the manioc. Other sources of it are the horse chestnut (*Aesculus Hippocastanum*), acorns (*Quercus* spp.) and one or two wild arums, including occasionally our own common British cuckoo-pint (*Arum maculatum*).

OILS AND FATS

We have already seen how the protein and carbohydrate reserves of plants are used as human food. The latter bulk much more largely in the picture, not only because they occur in greater absolute quantities, but also because human dietary is mixed and most of the necessary proteins are obtained from animal sources. We have also seen that plant proteins and carbohydrates have very little use except as food, laundry starch being the only example that comes to mind readily. The case of the vegetable oils is different. In one sense they are like the proteins in that their direct use as human food is relatively small, because the necessary supplies of fats are more easily absorbed from animal sources, but they differ very much from proteins and carbohydrates in that they have a very great number of industrial uses. Hence, although a number of vegetable oils do give extremely valuable human foods, a much larger number are exploited for other reasons and these are very varied. The distribution of the oils and fats within the plant body is also somewhat unlike that of the other two classes. Proteins occur all over the plant, and so do carbohydrates, although they are often specially abundant in storage organs, particularly vegetative organs. Most oils and fats, on the other hand, occur in economic quantity only in a particular type of storage tissue—that of seeds, where they are among the commonest of reserve materials. The one notable exception to this will be referred to in due course. The reason for this restriction is a simple one. Oil is an extremely convenient method of storing comparatively large amounts of potential energy in very small compass, and is thus one of the most suitable substances for seed reserves where a proper balance has to be struck between the provision of adequate supplies for the young plant and limitation of bulk for purposes of seed dispersal.

To understand the real importance of vegetable oils and fats it is necessary to consider their chemistry a little. Broadly speaking, there are two great classes of vegetable oils—the fatty oils and the essential oils. The former are by far the more important: the latter are for the most part, as their name implies, of use only as essences or flavourings. Fatty oils are, chemically, compounds of the alcohol (organic base), glycerol, and fatty acids. Glycerol is more familiarly known as glycerine and the fatty oils may accurately be termed glycerides. In the few vegetable waxes the compounds are similar except that the alcohol concerned is a higher alcohol than glycerol. Essential oils have a more complicated chemistry, and it must suffice here to say that three kinds may be recognised, viz. terpenes or hydrocarbon oils, aromatic aldehydes, and esters or organic salts. The essential oils differ also from the fatty oils in being volatile, a characteristic which causes them to evaporate entirely if exposed long enough to air. For this reason they do not leave behind them the "grease-spots" of the fatty oils.

The Uses of Vegetable Oils

The employment of vegetable oils as a special source of human foods is practically confined to the manufacture of margarine which, in the last fifty years, has become for many purposes a serious rival to butter and lard. Of course many other plant food-stuffs contain oils and fats, but these are consumed incidentally and not particularly. Margarine originated in response to an offer by the French Government of a prize for a cheap but suitable butter substitute. At first animal fats were used almost exclusively in its manufacture, but large quantities of vegetable fats are now employed, especially in the cheaper sorts.

Vegetable oils are also much used in soap manufacture. Soaps are certain metallic salts of the fatty acids and are, therefore, closely related to the natural oils, and the conversion of one into the other consists simply of the replacement of the glycerol by a metallic element. Sodium and potassium are those chiefly used, the former giving hard soaps and the latter soft soaps. The process is called saponification. Almost every kind of animal and vegetable oil has been used in soap-making and some of the latter are of special importance in the making of toilet soaps.

Certain vegetable fatty oils, if left in contact with the air, oxidise and form an elastic film on the surface, and this protects the remainder of the oil below. These oils are, for this reason, known as drying oils, and this peculiar property is the basis of much of the paint industry, where it is necessary to have substances which are normally liquid but which will harden off if applied in thin layers.

Other fatty oils do not undergo this oxidation but remain liquid in air permanently. This, and the fact that they are non-volatile, and are not easily decomposed by heat or cold, makes them of great value in the making of lubricants. Both animal and vegetable oils are used in this way.

A use confined to oils obtained from plants is their employment in the manufacture of oil cake for cattle feeding. The oils required for the purposes mentioned in the preceding paragraphs are obtained from the plant organs that contain them, usually seeds, by extraction and crushing. This readily yields a large proportion of the oils contained, but the last few percentages cannot be extracted without undue and uneconomic trouble. The seed residue containing this is therefore made up into fodder by milling and pressing into cake. This cake, containing as it does some of the oil and most of the other reserve foods of the seeds, is a very valuable stock feed.

These are the commoner uses of fatty vegetable oils, but there are several minor uses too. Colza oil (*q.v.*) is, or was, used extensively as an illuminant; olive oil is used in cooking, and others are medicinal.

Essential oils are the exception to the rule that vegetable oils are found almost exclusively in seeds, and they occur, usually in very small quantities, all over the plant and especially in the vegetative parts. In fact almost everywhere *but* in the seeds. They are seldom nutritious but are of great value on account of the aromatic substances they contain. They are therefore used almost entirely in two ways, for flavourings or essences and for perfumes. Occasionally they are used as drugs, and one (turpentine) is a useful solvent. Many of the plants containing them, such as the herbs of the old cottage gardens, are of age-old cultivation and sentiment. In early days, when sanitation was more imperfect than it is to-day, the value of herbs was a very real one in helping to overcome smells and to sweeten the air. It was also believed that they had a definite antiseptic effect. An orange stuffed with herbs and spices used sometimes to be carried and sniffed at intervals by people who were obliged to pass through insanitary places, and there is a well-known picture by Gilbert of Cardinal Wolsey going in procession to Westminster Hall holding one of these to his nose. A similar usage, dating from the time of gaol-fever, still persists in the carrying of nosegays of fragrant herbs by judges at the Old Bailey. Advances in chemistry have further lessened the importance of natural essential oils, and many which were previously obtainable only from plants can now be synthesised in the laboratory.

The essential oils are generally extracted from the plant by distillation, maceration, expression or enfleurage. The last is an uncommon process used in perfumery and depends on the fact that certain true fats tend to absorb appreciable quantities of essential oils. It is used mostly for delicate flower perfumes. The opening buds are left lying on the surface of lard or suet for two or three days, after which they are removed and the upper layer of the fat scraped off. The process is repeated until all the fat has absorbed the perfume to its maximum capacity.

Vegetable Fats

Under this heading are included the oils and fats whose chief use is directly or indirectly for human foods or for soaps.

First among these are the products of two palms, the coconut (*Cocos nucifera*) and the African oil palm (*Elaeis guineensis*). The oil is in each case extracted from the endosperm, but in the coconut this is so large that it is separated and dried before shipment. In this condition it is known as "copra". The oil-palm seeds are crushed whole. The coconut is grown all over the tropics, but the commercial supply comes chiefly from Ceylon, India and Malay. The great bulk of the supply of palm oil comes from wild African trees, but a little is grown in Asia. A ton of seeds yields up to nine hundred pounds of crude oil.

One fatty oil is more familiar than important. This is macassar oil from *Schleichera trijuga*, an Asiatic plant. The oil was formerly credited with great virtues as a hair restorer and its popularity necessitated the invention of the antimacassar, an amenity which has now outlived its usefulness.

The remaining vegetable fats are not very familiar though they are often of value in particular circumstances. Cocoa butter has been mentioned already as a by-product in the preparation of cocoa. Shea butter is from the seeds of an African tree, *Butyrospermum Parkii*; koma butter from another African tree, *Pentadesma butyracea*; kokune butter comes from the seeds of the mangosteen; nutmeg butter from the seeds of *Myristica argentea*; and there are others.

MAP 3

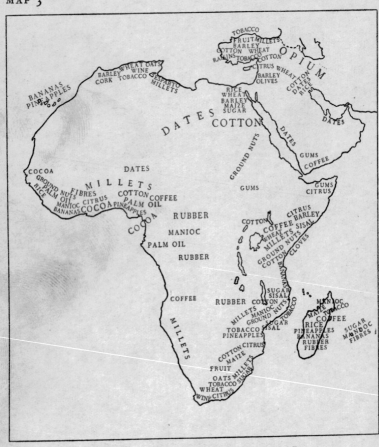

AFRICA, ARABIA AND ASIA MINOR

Chaulmoogra oil and Hydnocarpus oil from *Taraktogenos Kurzii* and species of *Hydnocarpus* respectively, all Asiatic plants, are of some value in the treatment of leprosy. The tracking down of the sources of these oils, which were already known by repute, in the forests of Burma, is a fascinating one, but the employment of the oils medicinally has not so far come up to expectation. Carapa oil from *Carapa guianensis* (tropical America), pongam oil from *Pongamia glabra* (eastern Asia), and cohune oil from the palm *Attalea Cohune* (central America), are noteworthy also. Chinese vegetable tallow comes from *Stillingia sebifera* and Japan wax from *Rhus succedanea*. Two Indian species of *Bassia* (*B. butyracea* and *B. latifolia*) also yield edible fats.

The only real vegetable wax of notable value is Carnauba wax from the tropical American palm, *Copernicia cerifera*. This differs from the other vegetable fats mentioned in that the organic alcohol in it is carnaubyl alcohol instead of glycerol. Candellila wax from the Mexican plant *Pedilanthus Pavonis* is a rather similar but less well-known product.

Drying Oils

By far the most extensively used of these oils is the product of a temperate plant, linseed or flax (*Linum usitatissimum*). The fibre flax comes from the same plant. It is widely cultivated in cool countries, sometimes primarily for its oil, sometimes for its fibre. British seed-oil supplies come mostly from the Argentine. Hemp (*Cannabis sativa*) is another plant yielding both fibre and seed-oil, but its exploitation for the latter is not very important. It is a plant of rather warmer countries than flax and much of it is grown in India. Other minor northern temperate sources of seed-oil are the walnut (*Juglans regia*), the opium poppy (*Papaver somniferum*) and the fruits of the sunflower (*Helianthus annuus*). The last is the most important of these and is widely cultivated in Russia, but the plant is a native of North America. It is said to give a very rich yield and its future as a crop is promising. Safflower oil is rather similarly obtained from the fruits of *Carthamus tinctorius*, a plant of Mediterranean lands.

The leading tropical drying oils are obtained from the nuts of a series of species belonging to the genus *Aleurites*. They are natives of tropical Asia and include tung oil (*A. Fordii*), Chinawood oil (*A. montana*), Japanese wood oil (*A. cordata*) and candlenut oil (*A. triloba*). Other Asiatic oil plants are *Perilla ocymoides* and *Gynocardia odorata*. From Africa come Niger oil (*Guizotia oleifera*), and America provides manihot oil (*Manihot Glaziovii*); oil from the seeds of the Brazil rubber tree (*Hevea brasiliensis*); and another poppy-seed oil (*Argemone mexicana*).

Semi-drying Oils

A few important oils are intermediate in character between the drying and the non-drying oils. The two leading sorts are of comparatively recent exploitation, namely cotton-seed oil and soya bean oil. Cotton-seed oil, which comes from the seed of the cotton plants (*Gossypium* spp.) yields as much as 35 gallons of oil per ton of seed, and yet for many years the seeds, after the removal of the cotton hairs, were treated as a useless waste product. To-day enormous quantities of the oil are used, especially in the oil-cake industry, and supplies come from almost all cotton-growing countries. Soya bean oil is also a modern commodity and, as we have seen, is only one of the numerous ways in which the plant is used.

Sesame oil comes from the seeds of a tropical herb, *Sesamum indicum*, now grown widely but originally native to eastern Asia, whence most of the supply still comes. Kapok seed (*Eriodendron anfractuosum*) also yields an oil very like that of the cottons, to which it is related.

Other sources of semi-drying oils are maize; an American herb *Madia sativa*; an Old World herb, *Camelina sativa*; and a tropical plant, *Croton Tiglium*.

Non-drying Oils

This group contains several very familiar oils. We may begin with the most temperate of them—rape or colza oil—from the seeds of *Brassica Napus*, which is grown for this purpose in many of the colder Eurasian countries. Colza is practically the only vegetable oil used as an illuminant and its popularity for this has now much decreased, but the oil is still employed largely for other purposes.

Next comes what is perhaps the best known of all the vegetable oils, olive oil, which is obtained from the stone and flesh of the drupaceous fruit of the olive tree (*Olea europaea*), a native of the Mediterranean countries. The part which the olive plays and has played in the lives of the peoples of these lands is shown by the repeated mention of the plant in myth and tradition. As early as the Flood it is associated with the dove sent out from the Ark by Noah, and it has always been a figure of speech as well as an emblem of peace. A crown of wild olive was in ancient Greece the reward of one who had deserved well of his country, and was also the highest prize of the Olympic games. The tree itself is an emblem of prosperity and fertility. The supplies of olive oil still come mostly from North Africa, Greece, Italy and Spain, but its cultivation has now spread to North and South America.

The medicinal reputation of castor oil rather obscures its more ordinary and, on the whole, more valuable uses. It comes from the seeds of the castor oil plant (*Ricinus communis*), a native of Africa but now grown all over the tropics. The seed is generally strangely marked and mottled and in shape also has a superficial resemblance to certain beetles. The oil is one of the most important items in the seed-crushing industry and is made use of in various ways.

Peanut oil is also among the first rank of oil-seed products, and is used not only for food but also for many commercial purposes. It comes from the seed of *Arachis hypogaea*, a plant already described under the pulses. The seed yields up to 30 per cent. oil.

Other important non-drying oils, most of them tropical, are rice oil, bitter-almond oil (*Prunus Amygdalus* var. *amara*), tea oil from *Camellia oleifera*, ben oil from *Moringa pterygosperma*, Sterculia oil from *Sterculia foetida*, and canary oil from *Canarium commune*. All these are Asiatic. Curcas oil is from the physic nut (*Jatropha Curcas*) of Barbados.

Essential Oils

There are hundreds of essential oils in use in different parts of the world, and there is space to mention only some of the commoner ones here. It is convenient to divide them into those used for flavourings and those used for perfumes, the former being the less numerous.

The best known oil flavours are from the *Citrus* fruits such as oil of lemon, oil of orange (from the sweet orange), oil of limes and oil of mandarins. Oil of peppermint and spearmint oil, the latter especially used for flavouring chewing-gum, come from two species of mint (*Mentha piperita* and *M. viridis*), both temperate herbs sometimes found wild in Britain. Juniper oil, which is used in gin-making, comes from the berry of *Juniperus communis*, also native to Britain and other northern countries. Wormwood oil has a somewhat unsavoury reputation because of its use in the spirit absinthe. It comes from *Artemisia Absinthium*, another native and northern species. The flavour of aniseed is afforded by two botanical products, the fruit of the true aniseed (*Pimpinella Anisum*), from the Orient, and the seeds of the star anise (*Illicium verum*), a plant of tropical Asia.

Three other tropical oils are also used as flavours, i.e. ginger oil (*Zingiber officinale*), oil of cloves (*Eugenia caryophyllata*) and pimento oil (*Pimenta officinalis*). Parts of these plants are themselves used as spices (see below).

First among the perfume oils is rose oil, or attar (corrupted into otto) of roses as it is called, obtained by the distillation of the flowers of *Rosa damascena*. The cultivation of the roses for this purpose was originally Persian but is now centred in Bulgaria. Absolutely pure and concentrated attar is very rare and valuable, and the ordinary product is frequently adulterated. Rose water is made from the flowers of *Rosa centifolia*.

Next come the series of oils of the citronella or verbena kind. Several plants contain oils of this type and perfume, but citronella oil proper comes from an Indian grass, *Andropogon Nardus*, while a close relation, *Andropogon citratus*, gives lemon-grass oil. Verbena oil is practically the same as the latter, but is obtained from *Lippia citriodora*, the American plant often seen in cold green-houses under the name "lemon-plant". A similar or identical oil occurs in the balm (*Melissa officinalis*).

The orange group again gives several good perfume oils. Neroli oil is extracted from the flowers of the bitter and sweet oranges; oil of petit grains is from their young shoots; and oil of bergamot is from the bergamot orange.

Another family specially characterised by abundance of essential oils is the lavender or dead-nettle family. Lavender oil and spike oil are from *Lavandula vera* and *Lavandula Spica* respectively, both Mediterranean plants; rosemary oil is from the European *Rosmarinus officinalis* and is used in the manufacture of eau-de-Cologne. Thyme oil is from *Thymus vulgaris* and *Thymus Serpyllum*, also European.

Then there is a group of plants whose flowers yield valuable perfumes when they are enfleuraged. Here belong the jessamine (*Jasminum grandiflorum*), the tuberose (*Polianthes tuberosa*), the jonquil (*Narcissus* spp.), the hyacinth (*Scilla* spp.) and the violets (*Viola* spp.). Oil of geranium is distilled from *Pelargonium odoratissimum*, a North African plant, and is sometimes used as a substitute for attar of roses. Oil of orris is from the rhizomes of *Iris florentina* and other spp. and these rhizomes when dry are known as orris root. Oil of wintergreen is an example of an essential oil now usually prepared synthetically; it was formerly obtained from the

North American plant, *Gaultheria procumbens*. Sassafras oil is from another North American plant, *Sassafras officinalis*.

We must be content to give merely a list of the more familiar essential oils obtained from tropical plants. There may be included patchouli oil from *Pogostemon Patchouly* (Asia), "costus" oil from *Aplotaxis Lappa* (India), zedoary from the rhizomes of *Curcuma Zedoaria* (Asia), Cassia oil from species of *Cassia*, ylang-ylang from *Cananga odorata* (Asia), linaloe oil from *Bursera* spp. (Mexico), oil of myrrh from *Commiphora* spp. (Asia and Africa), opopanax oil from *Opopanax Chironium* (Mediterranean), and frangipani from *Plumeria acutifolia* (India). Spikenard is the perfume from the rhizome of *Nardostachys Jatamansi*, a Himalayan plant.

A few essential oils are used more as drugs than otherwise. Oil of camphor is one of the most important of these. It comes from a large tree (*Cinnamomum Camphora*) which will be referred to later. Eucalyptus oil, of which there are many kinds, has a somewhat similar use and, like the cajuput oil from *Melaleuca* spp., comes from trees native to Australia.

Many other plants are commonly used in cooking to give flavour and in most cases the flavour is due to an essential oil, although it is not deliberately extracted or concentrated. Such are sage (*Salvia* spp.), marjoram (*Origanum vulgare*), hyssop (*Hyssopus officinalis*), bay (*Laurus nobilis*), fennel (*Foeniculum vulgare*), samphire (*Crithmum maritimum*) and many more. Hops, which are the floral bracts of the hop vine (*Humulus Lupulus*), have a special use in flavouring beer.

SPICES

It is a very short step from the essential oils to the spices, and in some ways an unnecessary one, since the value of most spices depends upon the fact that they contain essential oils. On the other hand, the spices are a familiar category of plant products and differ actually from the oils in that they are plant tissues themselves and not extracts from them.

The main function of spices has always been to flavour and

make palatable other food which normally is insipid or of unpleasant taste, and this was the origin of the trade in these commodities. In mediaeval and rather later times food was much more monotonous than now and very much more likely to be stale, and anything which tended to improve the taste and to disguise unpleasantness was particularly welcome. Hence the spices became of great value and were much desired.

The story of the spice trade is a very interesting one. Spices for the most part come from plants growing wild in tropical east Asia and, until the discovery of the passage to India by way of the Cape of Good Hope, the only supplies available were those brought with great danger and at great expense across the Asiatic continent. They were therefore comparatively rare, and as the demand for them increased became of quite fictitious value. With the opening up of the ocean route to the east it became possible to augment the supply considerably and, while their high value lasted, the spice trade was an extraordinarily profitable one. So much so that it soon became a subject of international strife, or at least armed competition. It was at the end of the fifteenth century that Vasco da Gama rounded the Cape and, sailing across the Indian ocean, founded trading settlements on the Indian coast, and for some time after the trade was the monopoly of the Portuguese. This lasted till about the beginning of the seventeenth century, but by then the power of Portugal had begun to wane and the trade passed gradually into the hands of the Dutch. Meanwhile England had also entered the lists and, after a long struggle for supremacy, much of the Dutch empire of the east passed into her hands, and she has held it since. Holland still retains large parts of the Malayan Archipelago, but Britain is the great colonial power in the East. The Asiatic possessions of the Portuguese have entirely vanished, except for a few scattered posts in India. The subsequent development of the British Empire in the East and in South Africa has been the result of many factors and events, but it must not be forgotten that it was originally the spice trade that inaugurated this most important chapter of human history.

The spices are interesting botanically as well as historically in the great range of plant organs of value in them. Cloves are the pedicels and unopened flower buds of the clove tree (*Eugenia caryophyllata*). This is a native of the Moluccas but is now cultivated extensively on the east coast of tropical Africa, although some of the supply still comes from the East. Allspice consists of the partially ripened fruits of the pimenta tree, *Pimenta officinalis*, rapidly dried, and is one of the few spices coming from the New World, in the tropical parts of which the tree is native. Peppers are the berries of climbing plants belonging to the genus *Piper*. Both black and white pepper comes from *Piper nigrum*, the latter being merely the former with the outer layers of the fruit removed; cubebs are the fruits of *Piper Cubeba*; betel pepper of *P. Betle* and the long pepper of *P. longum*. All these species are natives of Asia. The nutmeg is the seed of the berry of *Myristica fragrans*, a native of the Moluccas. The seed has a ruminate endosperm and is surrounded with a net-like aril from which another spice, mace, is obtained. The nutmeg, like the peppers, is now cultivated widely in the tropics. Vanilla comes from the long pods of a tropical epiphytic orchid, *Vanilla planifolia*, the only example of a major commercial product from this family.

Cardamoms are the seeds of another monocotyledon, *Elettaria Cardamomum*, from India and Ceylon, while grains of paradise are the seeds of a closely related plant, *Amomum* sp., from the same part of the world. Coriander, cummin and caraway each consists of the mericarps of three members of the carrot family from the Mediterranean region, *Coriandrum sativum*, *Cuminum Cyminum* and *Carum Carvi*. Capers are the flower buds of *Capparis spinosa*, also Mediterranean. Cinnamon is the dried bark of the younger twigs of an Asiatic tree, *Cinnamomum zeylanicum*, and cassia bark is from a second species of the same genus, *Cinnamomum Cassia*. Ginger is the dried rhizomes of *Zingiber officinale*, another Indo-Malayan monocotyledonous herb. Curry powder is a mixture of several spices including cinnamon, ginger, pepper and caraway. It contains also fenugreek (the seeds of a pulse, *Trigonella Foenum-graecum*) and curry leaves, the foliage of *Murraya Koenigii*.

There may also be mentioned here the various candied plant products. Angelica stands alone in being a stem product, from *Archangelica officinalis*, a plant of temperate Eurasia. The others are mostly fruit peels, particularly of oranges, lemons and citrons and include also the cherry. Certain flowers, especially violets, are also candied and used as ornaments and flavourings in confectionery. Other candied fruits, usually called crystallized fruits, because the sugar which preserves them is actually crystalline, are popular as sweetmeats.

Chapter IX

TIMBER, COAL AND PETROLEUM

TIMBER

If we take into account the whole range of its manifold uses there is little doubt that we must place timber next to actual foods as the plant product of most importance to man, if for no other reason than that it affords him a large measure of his shelter and warmth. It is true that the part played by timber in human economics tends rather to lessen with increasing civilisation, but no community has yet reached the stage at which it ceases still to be of almost first-rate value.

It is convenient to introduce the subject by a survey of the uses of timber, and then to go on to consider the various plants from which the supply comes.

Wood has four main uses. First its employment as a structural material, in which it is used in a more or less natural condition as it comes from the plant body. A moment's consideration will suffice to realise some of the innumerable ways in which it plays a part in everyday life. It is used to a considerable extent in almost all building operations and in some directions, as for temporary buildings, is all important. Furniture has always been made almost exclusively of wood and, although nowadays metal is occasionally used, there is no serious prospect of it rivalling wood. A large amount of timber is used in mining for the supply of the pit props by which the galleries are supported. Railways also consume a great deal in their sleepers, and here again metal has never yet proved a serious rival. Wood is also an ideal material for containers of all kinds, from cigar-boxes to coffins; much is consumed in the manufacture of casks and barrels; and fences, gates, hurdles and palings are all habitually made of wood. Woods of particular grain and colour have always been favourite articles for decorative purposes, and the number of them available has, by the introduction of many tropical timbers, been much increased of late years. Wooden vehicles, carpentry, games and toys, umbrellas and walking-sticks, and handles for tools and implements of all kinds are still further uses, and we must not forget that the briar pipe is of the same material (from a species of heath, *Erica arborea*). Apart from all these a great amount of wood, which is practically valueless for other purposes, is burnt as fuel. Finally cork and its manifold uses may reasonably be included, since it is obtained from the bark of certain trees.

The second great use of wood is in the manufacture of paper and cardboard. Before the middle of the last century most paper was made chiefly from rags but, as demand increased, other sources became necessary. Very soon the manufacture of paper from wood-pulp became established and this is to-day by far the greatest source of supply. For this purpose softwoods (see below) are generally used, and the countries where there are copious supplies of these are the great sources of the industry as, for example, Canada and the northern countries of Europe and Asia. Enormous quantities of timber are consumed in the production of the wood-pulp from which the paper is made and it is said that one edition of a large cheap daily newspaper consumes the timber of ten acres of forest.

Recent as the wood-pulp industry is, the third great use of timber is even more modern. This is the rayon or artificial silk industry, in which wood is now much the most important raw material, although other plant substances play some part. Artificial silk was actually first invented, if that word may be used, in France about forty years ago, but the original process, which depended on cotton, has been superseded by others. To-day by far the most important of these is the viscose process, in which wood is the raw material. The growth of the artificial silk industry, and especially its identification with our own country, is one of the great industrial developments of the post-war years. In 1907 the amount produced in this country was negligible; in 1912 it amounted to 3 million pounds; in 1924 it had risen to 25 million pounds and in 1928 to 54 million pounds, of which more than three-quarters was the result of the viscose process. In the last-named year the value of our export trade in artificial silk was about £8 million. To-day the world production of artificial silk annually is about 350 million pounds weight. The U.S.A. is the greatest producing country, and Great Britain comes next, but a great many countries manufacture some appreciable amount, including even Japan—the home of natural silk production.

The fourth use of timber is in the production of a great range of chemical substances which are obtained by its destructive distillation. If wood is strongly heated in a closed receptacle, a mixture of gases, a watery acid solution called pyroxylic acid, and wood tar are given off, and charcoal remains behind. The wood gases are in many ways like those given off by coal but they are of less importance, although they have on occasion been used as illuminants. The pyroxylic acid consists of a mixture of substances from which a number of valuable products can be separated. The most important of these are acetic acid, which is used both as a solvent and in the manufacture of vinegar and colours; methyl alcohol; and acetone. Methyl alcohol, sometimes called wood spirit, is useful as a solvent in various commercial processes, but it is best known when mixed with ordinary or ethyl alcohol to give methylated spirit. Its presence in this is intended to make the mixture so nauseous as to be undrinkable, but this desirable end is not always obtained. Acetone is another solvent and is used also in the manufacture of several articles, notably cordite, for which reason it was extremely important during the War. The wood tar is chiefly of value as a source of creosote which, in turn, has great uses on account of its antiseptic qualities. Certain other substances are also obtained from wood tar, and the ultimate product is pitch, itself quite a worthy substance.

In discussing commercial timbers there are certain purely botanical matters with which we must first concern ourselves.

It was stated in the introductory chapter that with one notable exception practically the whole range of commercial plant commodities is derived from plants belonging to the great group of the Angiosperms or Flowering Plants. This exception is that a considerable portion of the whole world timber supply is afforded by members of a distinct but rather similar group of plants, the Conifers or Gymnosperms. Certain characters of these two groups of plants are important in relation to the kind of wood they produce. The wood or xylem of the Angiosperms is comparatively heterogeneous, being composed of several kinds of cells, notably vessels, tracheids and fibres. The wood of Gymnosperms, on the other hand, is much more homogeneous because it is composed almost entirely of tracheids and has no vessels. Owing to this difference the timber of the Angiosperms is usually harder than that of the Gymnosperms, and is therefore known as hard-wood as opposed to the soft-wood provided by the Conifers. For some purposes hard-woods are essential, for others soft-woods are best. It must not be supposed that all hard-woods are markedly harder than all soft-woods, but the distinction generally holds good and the two terms are a useful means of distinguishing between the two types.

It also happens that the two kinds are to some extent segregated geographically. The soft coniferous woods occur in enormous quantities in the colder, and particularly the sub-arctic, zones of the world where they often form huge forests which contain few or no hard-wood trees. Conversely, in the warmer parts of the world, hard-woods very greatly predominate and such soft-woods as do occur tend to be rather sporadic.

Furthermore in regions of coniferous forests single tree species habitually cover wide areas to the exclusion of all other species so that what the foresters call "pure stands" result, and this is a great advantage in exploiting the trees. In hard-wood forests the mixture of species over areas of any size is always much greater. This is specially so in the tropics where usually a large number of different species grow thoroughly mixed together. As a result, it is generally much more costly to exploit hard-wood sources and frequently a comparatively small yield of the timber of one particular species represents the harvest of a large forest.

Timber also differs from most other kinds of plant products because the supplies tapped are nearly all natural ones, or have been up to the present. Certainly great areas have been deliberately forested but these represent rather supplies of the future. They mark a kind of plant culture which will assuredly become more and more vital as time goes on. The greatest timber areas of the world are those of the northern temperate regions and this is also the zone which has been most completely colonised by man in later centuries. We can hardly blame the early settlers for imagining that the illimitable forest represented an inexhaustible supply of timber, and they can scarcely have been expected to foresee the present consumption of wood. Because of this the virgin forests were as a rule exploited with a view to immediate convenience and economy of labour with the result that now the world is in danger of facing a definite shortage of timber. This lack of foresight has characterised most timber industries in the past, but the results have been particularly unfortunate in North America. The exhaustion of the natural reserves in that continent is clearly in sight unless there is some radical change in procedure. It is useless to cry over what is now spilt milk, but the position makes a sound policy of future afforestation one of the foremost considerations in the agricultural policy of nearly all highly civilised countries. In Britain for instance a large and comprehensive planting programme is gradually being carried out, not only to restore the woodlands which were felled during the War, but to yield a large future increase in production.

Since timber comes so largely from wild trees of which there are innumerable different species, it is not surprising to find that a considerable number have been investigated and used as sources of commercial woods. In the British Empire alone over 500 species of trees yield timber with some market value, and this list would be greatly increased if the whole world was taken into consideration.

The clear distinction between soft-woods and hard-woods and the marked geographical segregation of the chief economic kinds of both types make it convenient to arrange our review of commercial woods on a geographical basis. We will therefore follow this method, beginning with the soft-woods.

Soft-woods

The soft-woods (Conifers) are found chiefly in the two great subarctic belts of Eurasia and North America. The timber obtained from them is used very largely for the paper-pulp industry and for artificial silk, but a good deal is consumed in the rougher and cheaper kinds of building construction.

The Soft-woods of Europe and Asia

The most important of these is the northern pine (*Pinus sylvestris*) which provides yellow and red deal. It comes chiefly from the countries round the White Sea and it is the same species which, better known as the Scots pine, is still found wild in a few parts of Scotland. Spruce (*Picea excelsa*) gives white deal or Baltic whitewood chiefly from northern Europe. Larch (*Larix europaea*) also provides a durable timber. Yew (*Taxus baccata*) is also employed to a limited extent, but is not now so valuable as in the days when bows were made from it.

Three species of pines from the south of Europe and the Mediterranean region also give a certain amount of timber. These are the cluster pine (*Pinus Pinaster*), the stone pine (*Pinus Pinea*) and the Corsican pine (*Pinus Laricio*). The first is the species which is so widely planted on the sandy soils of the south of England. The seeds of the second species are edible and are known as pignolias. The wood of the true cedars (*Cedrus* spp.), from North Africa, Syria and North India, is sometimes employed commercially.

The Soft-woods of North America

The soft-wood species of the New World are much more numerous than those of the Old World and afford a much wider range of timbers. They fall roughly into two groups, those of Canada east of the Rocky Mountains and those of British Columbia and the Pacific coast generally.

Of the former the most important and widespread are the white or Weymouth pine (*Pinus Strobus*) and the Canadian spruce (*Picea alba*), and from them come the great bulk of the wood-pulp supplies. The pitch pine (*Pinus palustris*), the red pine (*P. resinosa*), the jack pine (*P. Banksiana*), the hemlock spruce (*Tsuga canadensis*) and the tamarack (*Larix americana*) are also of considerable value.

Of the latter, the Columbian or Oregon pine is the chief. These are actually the names given to the wood of the Douglas fir (*Pseudotsuga Douglasii*) and illustrates the important point that the names of the timbers may have little or nothing to do with the name of the species that bears them. It is one of the largest conifers, often reaching 200 feet in height, and is in this respect only exceeded by the western white cedar (*Thuja gigantea*), and the two redwoods (*Sequoia gigantea* and *S. sempervirens*), which may reach a height of 350 or even 400 feet. All these three give valuable timbers, but the supplies of the two last are very restricted and the trees occur only over a very small area.

Besides these several other species are valuable in lesser degree and of them may be mentioned the sugar pine (*Pinus Lambertiana*), the pencil or red cedar (*Juniperus virginiana*), the Port Orford cedar (*Cupressus Lawsoniana*), Engelmann's spruce (*Picea Engelmannii*), the western larch (*Larix occidentalis*), the yellow cedar (*Chamaecyparis nootkatensis*), the lodge-pole pine (*Pinus contorta*), the loblolly pine (*P. Taeda*), and various firs (*Abies* spp.).

A few southern hemisphere Conifers also afford small supplies of timber, especially for local consumption. Among

MAP 4

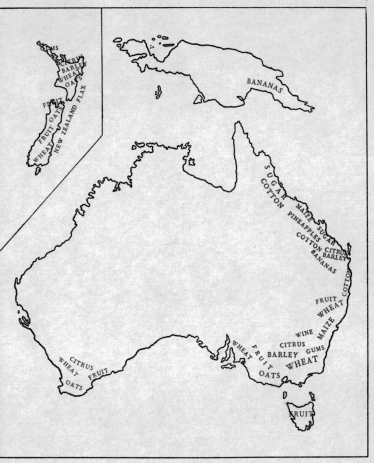

AUSTRALIA, NEW ZEALAND AND NEW GUINEA

MAP 4

the more notable are the kauri pine (*Agathis australis*) and the New Zealand white pine (*Podocarpus dacrydeoides*), the latter being especially used for the making of boxes for the export trade in butter. Other species of the genus *Podocarpus* are used too, both in Australasia and South Africa.

HARD-WOODS

A description of the hard-wood timbers of commerce is a much more lengthy process because there are many more of them and they are for the most part available in considerably smaller quantities. Their great use is in the better classes of constructional work where the great variation in their appearance and physical features often makes them of special value. They show great differences in density, grain, surface and colour, and all kinds of desirable aesthetic effects can be obtained by using appropriate kinds. For instance, many comparatively rare tropical woods have recently secured a place in the markets as materials for expensive panellings and veneerings.

The Hard-woods of the North Temperate Old World

Into this category fall all the species which are native to our own country and therefore particularly familiar to English readers both as timbers and in a living condition.

Pride of place in any list must go to the oak, of which there are many varieties, mostly coming from the species *Quercus Robur*. Commercially they are distinguished as English oak (the least plentiful), Australian oak, Russian oak and Japanese oak, the latter being the product of several species. They are among the oldest timbers of commerce and still retain much of their pre-eminence despite the ever-increasing numbers of competitors. English oak, however, has had its heyday in the times when the wooden warships it went to build formed the first line of national defence. Nowadays the slowness of its growth limits its supply very much and it is largely replaced, wherever possible, by other timbers.

The walnut (*Juglans regia*) is perhaps the timber which approaches most nearly to oak in value and prestige and in some ways, as for furnishing, it even takes precedence. It comes chiefly from Europe and western Asia and is also much used for veneers. Next to walnut in utility comes a whole series of more or less familiar timbers, of which the more important are elm (*Ulmus campestris*), lime or linden (*Tilia cordata*) specially favoured by the wood carver, ash (*Fraxinus excelsior*) for furniture, beech (*Fagus sylvatica*) especially used for chairs, hornbeam (*Carpinus Betulus*), sycamore (*Acer Pseudo-Platanus*) and birch (*Betula alba*). The wood of several species of willow (*Salix* spp.) and poplar (*Populus* spp.), the alder (*Alnus glutinosa*), the plane (*Platanus orientalis*), the horse chestnut (*Aesculus Hippocastanum*) and the sweet chestnut (*Castanea sativa*) are also valuable. The latter is often grown in south-eastern England under coppice conditions for hop poles, and the hazel (*Corylus avellana*) is similarly grown for hurdles. Last comes a group of smaller and less plentiful trees like the holly (*Ilex Aquifolium*), the pear (*Pyrus communis*), the apple (*Pyrus Malus*), the box (*Buxus sempervirens*) and the olive (*Olea europaea*). The box is a particularly hard and close-grained wood and has special uses where these features are valuable. Of recent years holly has suffered a great eclipse because its uses were nearly all in connection with horse transport.

The Hard-woods of the North Temperate New World

The list of species in this heading is practically the same, as regards timbers, as that in the preceding except that the actual species concerned are generally different, being the American counterparts of those just mentioned. The most important are the American oaks (*Quercus alba* and *Q. rubra*), the black walnut (*Juglans nigra*), the basswood (*Tilia americana*), the maples (*Acer* spp.), the rock elm (*Ulmus racemosa*), the cotton woods (*Populus* spp.), the ash (*Fraxinus americana*), and the birch (*Betula Lenta*). Besides these there is a group of peculiarly American woods for the most part interchangeable in use with those already cited. Prominent among them are the hickories (*Carya* spp.), the whitewood (*Liriodendron tulipifera*), the satin walnut (*Liquidambar styraciflua*), the tupelo (*Nyssa sylvatica*), and the Virginian date plum (*Diospyros virginiana*). The wood of certain species of *Magnolia* is now employed successfully to some extent in cabinet making.

Partly because of their proximity to the great centres of population and partly because they are, in general more abundant, the temperate hard-woods occupy, with one or two notable exceptions, a larger place economically than the tropical kinds, and this gives rather a false impression of their actual relative values as timber. Many of the tropical hard-woods afford very fine timber, but difficulties of collection and transport are such that they have only a limited and local consumption. Many of them, if they could be marketed conveniently, would prove formidable rivals to the common temperate sorts.

Another consideration that tends to hinder the wider employment of many tropical hard-woods is the difficulty of identifying accurately the trees from which they come, and popular and trade names are usually applied to them so loosely that it is not easy to be certain of the exact nature of the products. Added to this there are, generally speaking, many more species concerned and even very closely related species do not always afford exactly equivalent timbers. General trade names often include the wood of quite a number of different trees. As far as possible below the trade and scientific names are both given but the latter are commonly less definite and certain than in the case of temperate trees, which can be so much more easily verified.

The Hard-woods of Tropical Asia

The first wood to be noticed here is teak (*Tectona grandis*), a native of Indo-Malay and especially of Burma. Taking all points of view into account, teak must rank as the finest and most valuable of all timbers. It is very dense and heavy and highly resistant, owing to the deposits of silica in its tissues, and it is most used for ship-building. It is too expensive and too heavy to be used very much in European joinery but it has a special use for the benches of laboratories, where its resistant character comes to the fore. Because of this teak is one of the most familiar of tropical woods to science students.

The family Leguminosae yields several very important timbers, including the Asiatic rosewoods (*Dalbergia latifolia* and other spp.), Amboyna wood (*Caesalpinia Sappan*) and padouk (*Pterocarpus indicus*). The fine grains of these make them of special value in ornamental work.

The family Dipterocarpaceae too yields valuable timbers. The trees from which they come are very large and often have particularly long, straight and unbranched trunks. Unfortunately it is difficult to make any very definite statements as to the species involved because their identification is very confused. There may, however, be mentioned yang, gurjun, eng, krabash (*Dipterocarpus* spp.), and the sal tree (*Shorea robusta*).

Indian satinwood comes from *Chloroxylon Swietenia* and is much used in cabinet making, and Indian cedar wood (*Cedrela Toona*) is used for cigar boxes.

The subject of ebony may be introduced here. Ebony is the name given to heart-wood which is very hard and black because of the deposits of gum resin in it. True ebony (*Diospyros Ebenum*) comes from India and Ceylon, but many other rather similar products exist throughout the tropics. True ebony is sometimes called Macassar ebony, a name familiarised, although in quite another connection, in the word antimacassar. In tropical Asia ebony-like woods come also from species of the genus *Dalbergia*, as well as from other species of *Diospyros* such as the Coromandel wood (*D. quaesita*).

The Hard-woods of Australia

These belong mostly to the huge genus *Eucalyptus* (gums), which include some of the tallest trees in existence, rivalling the redwoods. Two kinds, jarrah (*E. marginata*) and kaui (*E. versicolor*) are fairly widely used but most are employed in the Australian continent itself. Jarrah has recently become popular for parquet floorings under the name of Australian oak and is also used for street paving and for level crossings, as it is very resistant to vibration.

Silky oak (*Grevillea robusta*), black bean (*Castanospermum australe*) and myall (*Acacia pendula*) are also important. Small individuals of the first-named are not uncommonly grown in our own country as decorative indoor plants.

The Hard-woods of Africa

Africa, of all tropical countries, contributes least to the timber trade, and nearly all the African woods centre round the vexed question of mahogany. The true mahogany is, as we shall see, an American tree, but there are several African trees whose timbers are sufficiently similar to give them much the same range of uses. The separation and recognition of the different sorts is at present very confused, and all that can be said here is that one of the most important is the so-called African mahogany (*Khaya senegalensis*).

Africa has also several ebony-like woods, mostly belonging to the Leguminosae. Of them one of the best known is African blackwood (*Dalbergia melanoxylon*).

There may also be mentioned here two valuable timbers which are natives of and much used in South Africa, stink-wood (*Ocotea bullata*) and black ironwood (*Olea laurifolia*). They are first-class furniture woods, as the early settlers soon discovered, but their employment is practically confined to their native country.

The Hard-woods of Tropical America

First and foremost among these is the real mahogany, known also as the Honduras mahogany or Spanish mahogany (*Swietenia Mahagoni*) from Central America and the West Indies. It was introduced into England about the year 1700 and its immediate success was primarily due to its use by the great furniture designer and maker Chippendale, who established it in what seems to be permanent popularity for these purposes. It is used also in certain branches of ship-building. Soon after the middle of last century the tree was introduced into eastern Asia.

In America, as in other parts of the tropics, Leguminous trees are valuable wood producers, and here belong partridge wood (*Andira* spp.), purpleheart (*Copaifera* spp.), American rosewood (*Dalbergia* spp.), mora (*Dimorphandra Mora*) and others. American ebony or cocus wood (*Brya Ebenus*) is also of this family.

Other valuable timbers are American satinwood (*Zanthoxylum* spp.), quassia (*Quassia amara*), lance wood (*Calycophyllum candidissimum*), crabwood (*Carapa guianensis*), tulip wood (*Physocalymma scaberrimum*), blue mahoe (*Hibiscus elatius*), ironbark (*Ixora ferrea*), and snakewood (*Brosimum Aubletii*). Special mention may be made of greenheart (*Nectandra Rodiaei*) from Guiana because of its beautiful texture, colour and grain.

Tropical timbers vary very much in weight, and two extremes may be exemplified from among American timbers. The wood of the lignum-vitae (*Guaiacum* spp.) is about 80 pounds to the cubic foot, so that it sinks in water. This is the heaviest of all woods. On the other hand, balsa wood (*Ochroma Lagopus*) is even lighter than cork, and is used for such purposes as surgical splints and in aeroplane construction. The lightness of the wood is due to the fact that the xylem is almost entirely parenchymatous with just a few very widely scattered vessels.

THE WOODY PRODUCTS OF MONOCOTYLEDONS

The virtual limitation of arboreal plants in this group to the one family of the palms and the peculiar anatomy of their stems make the Monocotyledons of very little value as timber. Occasionally palm wood, of one kind or another, is used in small work where rather bizarre effects are desired, and palm trunks are commonly employed in native house building, but this is all.

There is, however, another family of Monocotyledons which includes a group of plants that furnish a woody product of the greatest value. These are the bamboos, which are found throughout the tropics and which include some very large plants. They may be considered here in general terms not only for their wood but for their other uses too.

The hollow, noded and rod-like stems of the bamboos seem almost specially designed for a multitude of uses, especially among the peoples of their native lands. In our own country we see them almost exclusively in the form of low-class furniture, or as sticks and canes, and we gain no impression of their immense utility in most parts of the tropics. The material we see is also very small, and it is difficult to realise that some species actually reach the height of our tallest native trees. The wood is very elastic and very hard owing to the deposit of silica, and the stems are therefore very light but strong and easily split. They are used in all kinds of structural work from bridge building to roofing tiles, and their hollowness invites another whole series of applications in tubular form such as water pipes, gutters, masts and various household utensils. Besides all these the wood can, when finely split, be woven into many useful articles like baskets, blinds and fans, and even into paper. In short, it is difficult to imagine a use to which they have not been or might not be put. Fibre gramophone needles are commonly made of bamboo wood, and it is even said that in the same kind of way the split stems can be used as blades in grass cutters, one of the very few instances of the use of wood instead of metal in machinery.

The largest of the bamboos belong to the genus *Dendrocalamus*, and their stems are usually employed whole in large-scale structural work. Nearly all the smaller kinds can be utilised to some extent, but the chief genera economically are *Melocalamus, Cephalostachyum, Ochlandra, Bambusa, Thyrsostachys* and *Thamnocalamus*.

CORK

Cork, although from a botanical point of view a cortical tissue, the phelloderm, is nevertheless the product of a woody stem, and may therefore be inserted here. The commercial cork is obtained from the thick bark of the cork oak (*Quercus Suber*), a native of the Mediterranean regions. The bark is composed of dead and water-tight cells and is, for its bulk, extremely light and buoyant, though without mechanical strength. Since the cells are empty it is capable of considerable compression, and it is to some extent elastic. Several other trees of various kinds produce a similar product, but these are not used much commercially.

VEGETABLE IVORIES

This also seems the most appropriate place to refer to a very peculiar series of plant products known as vegetable ivories. Their name indicates that they can be used in certain circumstances for the well-known real animal ivory. They consist of the very hard and white endosperms of the seeds of several species of palms. They come especially from the genera *Phytelephas* (tropical America), *Nipa* (Malay) and *Borassus* (Africa) and many others yield them too, but they are used as curiosities more than anything else. Their small bulk prevents them from being of any very great importance, though they have several minor uses.

COAL

We had occasion a few pages previously to refer to the use of timber as fuel. It is perhaps not always realised that of the other two great sources of fuel, coal and petroleum, the former is certainly and the latter probably a plant product.

Coal is the fossilised remains of vegetation that lived long ages ago in former geological periods. It is now usually so altered that all obvious botanical structure is lost, but microscopic examination shows that it is composed almost entirely of plant tissues which have been converted, in the course of time, more or less completely into carbon.

Coal is by no means all of one kind. It takes a very long time for plant remains to become completely fossilised, that is to say, to reach the final stage in the total conversion of the original plant structures into mineral matter, and different kinds of coal vary greatly according to the length of time that the process has been going on. The oldest coals, those derived from the earlier geological formations, approach the real fossil condition most nearly, but the later and more recent the deposit and the shorter the time it has been forming, the smaller proportion of carbon it contains. Anthracite contains about 95 per cent. of carbon, but most coals have less than this and some much less.

In the earlier stages of coal formation the product is generally brown rather than black, is comparatively soft, and shows a greater degree of plant structure. Material of this kind is called lignite or brown coal, and is plentiful in some countries such as Germany, but it has nothing like the same value as hard black coal. Peat is a still earlier condition in the conversion of plant tissues into coal and consists of the remains of plants which have lived very recently. It can, however, be used conveniently as coal in countries where, as in Ireland, deposits of brown or hard coal are not available. Peat is constantly being formed to-day by the death of vegetation where there are certain suitable climatic conditions, and this peat will, if left undisturbed, become gradually converted into real coal.

The geographical distribution of coal deposits is not at all even. Some countries have vast supplies—others have none or only a little of inferior quality. Great Britain is especially fortunate in this matter, because her coalfields are not only very extensive but contain coal that is very old and which therefore makes a high grade fuel.

The importance of coal in modern highly organised civilisations can scarcely be over-estimated. The possession of great coalfields means the possession of a vast store of comparatively cheap power and heat, and makes possible all kinds of industries which would otherwise be impracticable. Its uneven distribution adds to its value to the countries which do possess it, because it thereby becomes a powerful bargaining and trade lever. It is probably true to say that a country without considerable national supplies of coal can never support a great industrialised population. Our own country is an outstanding example of its importance, since coal supports most of our heavy industries and by exporting the surplus of our production we pay for much of the food-stuffs which we must needs buy for our people. In fact to such an extent is our civilisation based on coal that this commodity has been called "the paramount lord of industry"—a title which it still retains despite the threat of more modern fuels.

British coal comes from deposits and beds that were laid down in the early geological period known as the Carboniferous, and is therefore very old and contains a high proportion of carbon. It is actually composed chiefly of the remains of large woody plants belonging to groups of the plant kingdom now represented only by the Club-Mosses and the Horsetails. These plants were, like their modern descendants, cryptogams, reproducing by means of spores, and these spores in countless myriads contribute very largely to the constitution of coal.

Coal is, of course, chiefly used as a direct source of heat and power, but it can also be made to yield a vast number of valuable chemical compounds. For this purpose it is distilled in very much the same sort of way as has been already described for wood. The products of this process are so numerous that they cannot possibly be listed here in full, and anything approaching a complete account of them must be sought in books on organic chemistry, but an outline of the results of distillation can be given.

The destructive distillation of coal results in five primary products—coal gas, light oil, coal tar, ammoniacal liquor and coke, the last being the ultimate residue. It is used as fuel and for the further manufacture of a number of important gases and solids. Coal gas is a very familiar illuminant and fuel and is almost always used in these ways. The light oil contains benzol, naphtha and other fuels and solvents and from them, apart from their direct use, a whole series of chemical substances, from perfumes to explosives, can be prepared. The ammoniacal liquor furnishes liquid ammonia, used widely in refrigeration, and can be used for the preparation of a number of ammonium salts, some of which are among the most valuable of artificial manures.

It is, however, the coal tar that is the greatest asset in the distillation of coal. Coal tar can, when further treated, be made to yield a series of oils—light, middle, heavy and green oils—and a residual deposit of pitch. The light oils are like those already mentioned and contain the same substances. The middle oils provide phenol (carbolic acid), cresol and naphthalene, all important preservatives and antiseptics. The heavy oils also yield phenol, and creosote in addition. The green oils give similar but less familiar products. Pitch can be obtained in various degrees of hardness and has innumerable uses for waterproofing, insulating and other forms of protection.

Valuable as is this series of direct products, it takes no account of the immense range of complex substances which can be prepared from them by further chemical treatment. The coal-tar dyes are the most familiar of these, but they by no means exhaust the possibilities and it would indeed be rash to state that any organic compound is entirely unobtainable either from coal tar or its derivatives.

PETROLEUM

Petroleum is another deposit of great geological age but, unlike coal, there remains no trace of its original structure, and there is far less agreement as to its origin. It was formerly considered to be purely inorganic in nature, but this view is now discarded and its organic derivation is to-day scarcely disputed. Whether it is entirely an animal product, entirely a plant product, or a mixture of the two is uncertain, but the most widely held opinion is that it has been formed, by enormous pressure and other agencies, from the minute floating life of shallow seas. If this is so, it is almost certainly composed of both plant and animal matter, but since the latter must have been dependent upon the former, we may justifiably regard it primarily as a plant product.

Petroleum or crude oil is, as it comes from the earth, a dark oily liquid with a characteristic smell. Chemically it is a mixture of substances, mostly hydrocarbons. Its distribution over the world is very scattered, and the most important sources are the oilfields of the U.S.A. and Mexico, South Russia, Rumania and Persia, in the order named.

Economically petroleum is the counterpart of coal, which indeed it has already supplanted in many directions. The crude product can be used in certain ways, and this direct employment is rapidly increasing, but the value of petroleum lies chiefly in the substances that can be obtained by its fractional distillation. The products of this process may be outlined as light oils, illuminating oils, lubricating oils and a tar residue, which is used in road-making and so on. The light oils are, above all, invaluable because they contain a high proportion of the motor fuel which Europeans call petrol and Americans call gasoline. The illuminating oils include kerosene, and the lubricating oils comprise a whole series of machine oils.

Vaseline and paraffin are other important products of petroleum and, if the temperature of distillation is high enough, a very pure form of coke is the end-product in place of tar.

It is difficult to write a readable running account of the products of distillation of wood, coal and coke, and they can be more satisfactorily realised in the following much simplified diagrams.

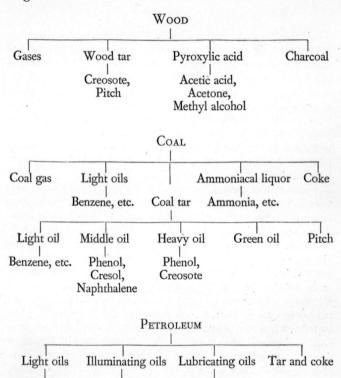

WOOD

| Gases | Wood tar | Pyroxylic acid | Charcoal |
| | Creosote, Pitch | Acetic acid, Acetone, Methyl alcohol | |

COAL

| Coal gas | Light oils | | Ammoniacal liquor | Coke |
| | Benzene, etc. | Coal tar | Ammonia, etc. | |

| Light oil | Middle oil | Heavy oil | Green oil | Pitch |
| Benzene, etc. | Phenol, Cresol, Naphthalene | Phenol, Creosote | | |

PETROLEUM

| Light oils | Illuminating oils | Lubricating oils | Tar and coke |
| Petrol (gasoline), etc. | Kerosene, etc. | Machine oils | |

Chapter X

RUBBER: RESINS, BALSAMS AND GUMS: TANS AND DYES: FIBRES

RUBBER

The rubber industries form one of the largest, and to-day perhaps the greatest, of the branches of commerce consuming raw materials of vegetable origin. It is also that with the shortest, but by no means the least eventful, history.

Rubber is prepared from the substance caoutchouc, which is present in the milky juice or latex of many plants. This juice is characteristic of certain families and genera of plants, such as the ligulate members of the daisy family, but rubber is manufactured almost exclusively from a very few woody plants belonging to other families. Chemically rubber is a hydrocarbon.

Rubber was first observed by the early explorers who visited South America, whence comes its first but misleading name of India-rubber. For long after this it was little more than a scientific curiosity, and it was really not until the middle of the nineteenth century that the discovery of the process known as vulcanising made possible its commercial use on a large scale. This process is a complicated one, but it consists essentially of treating the raw rubber with sulphur. Its effect is greatly to increase the range of temperatures over which the rubber retains its characteristic pliability and plasticity. Unless so treated it tends, when much heated or cooled, to lose these and to become sticky or brittle, a disadvantage seriously limiting its usefulness. Even with the discovery of vulcanisation rubber did not immediately become of great importance, and a further circumstance was necessary to usher in its world wide use. This was the almost simultaneous development of two other great new industries—those of electrical equipment and motor cars and bicycles. In the last twenty-five years the world's consumption of rubber has increased tenfold.

For a long time after its value was first realised, the only considerable source of rubber was the Brazilian or Pará rubber tree (*Hevea brasiliensis*), which grew wild in great numbers in that and other parts of tropical South America, and these were exploited to the limit. Unfortunately, although to some extent unavoidably, the exploitation was carried out in a most un-economic way. Collectors were sent out into the forests wholesale and the rubber was collected in all sorts of ways without any regard to the fate of the trees or the future of the supply. Not only this but the method adopted could only be made remunerative by the employment of the very cheapest kinds of labour. As a result, the employment conditions of the native races, from whom the industry was recruited, soon became atrociously bad and only in word distinguishable from slavery. This, together with the wasteful methods used, quickly led to a widespread search for other and more con-venient sources of supply.

In the course of this search it was found that a number of woody plants native to tropical Africa also yielded appreci-able amounts of good quality rubber, and attention was soon turned to them. These plants grew mostly in the basin of the Congo, and this region, known at the time as the Congo Free State, became the centre of the new industry. Here circum-stances of labour and collection again lead to the terrible sort of conditions which had prevailed in America, and the Congo gained an unfortunate notoriety. Indeed things became even worse than they had been in America, and it finally became necessary for an international enquiry to investigate them. Ultimately the Congo Free State was taken over by the Belgian government and became the Belgian Congo of to-day.

African rubber differs from Pará rubber, as the product of the Brazilian tree is called, in certain minor features of in-dustrial importance and comes from quite different plants.

These are all woody plants, and the best known of them are *Funtumia elastica* and various species of the genus *Landolphia*. In the former, as in the Pará rubber, the latex is collected from the stems by incisions in the bark, but in the latter it comes from the rhizomes and the plants are usually destroyed in the process.

While this rather crude method of gaining rubber was going on in South America and Africa, strenuous efforts were being made to obtain seeds or young trees of the Brazilian plant so that its deliberate cultivation could be established in suitable parts of the world. After many vicissitudes seeds and plants were brought to England and here the former were germinated. The seedlings were then transported to Malay, where it was supposed that the climate would suit them, and there they soon became established. From this small beginning there developed the great supplies of plantation-grown rubber which have now almost completely superseded the wild product. In 1924 plantation rubber accounted for 93 per cent. of the world production. British Malaya has by far the greatest area of rubber plantations, with Java and Sumatra next, followed by Ceylon.

Rubber can be obtained from many other trees besides those mentioned, and some of these have been used to a certain extent in increasing supplies, but none compete seriously with *Hevea brasiliensis*. Ceara rubber comes from *Manihot Glaziovii*, a native of America and a close relation of the plant that gives tapioca and cassava. Assam rubber is the product of *Ficus elastica*, a kind of fig with very dark green shining leaves which is often grown in a young condition as a hothouse or indoor plant in Britain. Panama rubber or ule is provided by *Castilloa elastica*, a Central American species. Pontianac or jelutong rubber is from *Dyera costulata*, a Malayan plant.

The great disadvantage of the tree rubbers is, of course, the length of time that must elapse before the crops are old enough to be tapped, and many attempts have been made to avoid this by obtaining rubber from herbaceous plant-species which would yield more frequently and would be easier to

MAP 5

NORTH AND CENTRAL AMERICA AND WEST INDIES

MAP 5

NORTH AND CENTRAL AMERICA AND WEST INDIES

grow. Guayule (*Parthenium argentatum*), a Central American member of the daisy family, has been most studied in this connection but its use has not become established. Species of *Asclepias* have also been regarded as hopeful products. The late Mr Edison directed a good deal of attention to this problem of herbaceous rubber plants towards the end of his life and is said to have gone far towards solving it, but up to the present commercial supplies of rubber come entirely from the woody plants described.

In addition to the true rubbers there are sundry rubber-like substances of some value. Gutta-percha, which differs from rubber in that it softens when heated and cannot be vulcanised, is the product of various members of the genus *Palaquium*, natives of Malay. Chicle is a gum with some of the properties of rubber from a similar but American tree *Achras Sapota*, and it is used in the making of chewing gum. Balata is a rubber-like substance from the American tree *Mimusops Balata*, still another related species.

RESINS, BALSAMS AND GUMS

The name resin is given to certain compounds of carbon, hydrogen and oxygen that occur naturally in plants and which are usually collected as exudations, but it is difficult to give any accurate definition of these substances unless we enquire into their chemistry more deeply than is justifiable here. They are generally divided into oleo resins and gum resins, and when first taken from the plants usually contain volatile aromatic constituents. In this state they are often referred to as balsams. Many of them have a medicinal value and some can be used as stains, but they are chiefly employed in the manufacture of varnishes, sealing-wax, poor grades of soap and the like. Gums are mucilaginous adhesive substances which dissolve in water and are related to the carbohydrates. They may occur associated with resin, as in the gum resins, or alone.

The products are all of fairly common occurrence in plants

and a number of them enter commerce. Of those which have a purely local reputation it is not possible to speak. The names resin, balsam and so on are, however, not applied with very much care and the classification used below, the ordinary commercial one, is not entirely scientific.

True Resins

The common resin or rosin, or colophony, is obtained from the sticky exudation of pine trees, notably from *Pinus australis* in North America, *Pinus Pinaster* in France and *Pinus longifolia* in India. The raw product as it leaves the trees is aromatic, and is known as crude turpentine. This is distilled in steam, the turpentine oil comes off, and the resin is left behind. Colophony is not a high-grade product and is used for cheap varnishes and soaps and for various chemical purposes.

Amber is a fossil resin, that is to say, it is a product of trees which have long been dead. These probably also belonged to the genus *Pinus*. During their life they produced resinous exudations and these have, by a gradual loss of water and subsequent hardening, become very resistant and now persist when the trees which bore them have long since passed away. It is found in many places but especially along the shores of the Baltic, whence it is occasionally washed up on the coasts of Britain.

The best and most valuable resins are those known as the copals. Of these there are several kinds, and they are used in making the best varnishes. East African copal is probably from species of the genus *Trachylobium*, West African copal comes from several species, including *Copaifera Guibourtiana*, and South American copal is from species of *Hymenaea*. Kauri copal or kauri gum, as it is more often called, is obtained from *Agathis australis*, a tree native to Australia and New Zealand, and related to the pines. Some of it comes, like amber, from trees now dead and is dug out of the soil in which these grew. The last and best of the copals is Manila copal from

Agathis Dammara, a Malayan species of the same genus. The name dammar resin is best applied to certain copal-like resins obtained from a number of Asiatic trees belonging to the family Dipterocarpaceae and especially from *Shorea odorata* (Burma).

The elemi resins form an important group of soft resins. They come from many parts of the world and from a variety of trees. Manila elemi and East Indian elemi are from species of the genus *Canarium*; African elemi is from *Boswellia Frereana*. Yucatan and Mexican elemi are from *Amyris Plumieri* and *A. elemifera* respectively, while Brazilian elemi comes from *Protium heptaphyllum*. Gommier resin, or gommart, is the produce of *Bursera gummifera*, a West Indian plant. The elemi resins used to have a medicinal value but are now used in varnishes and printing inks.

The acaroid resins, of which there are two, red and yellow, come from species of the genus *Xanthorrhoea*. These are Australian plants, and among the comparatively few arboreal monocotyledons other than the palms. The resins are used for sealing-wax and varnishes and give a red stain. Sandarac resin, with rather similar uses, comes from the conifer *Callitris quadrivalvis* of North Africa. Mastic resin, used in lithography, is from *Pistacia Lentiscus*, a Mediterranean and Asiatic tree. Guaiacum resin, from *Guaiacum officinale* (tropical America), podophyllin resin from *Podophyllum peltatum* (North America) and *P. Emodi* (Asia) are medicinal only. Stains are obtained from the dragon's blood, a resin from *Daemonorops Draco* (Malay) and from the Socotra dragon's blood (*Dracaena cinnabari*).

We may conclude our account of the true resins by referring shortly to the shellacs. These resins are actually obtained from an insect, the lac insect, but they have a botanical interest because several plants are specially cultivated as the food of these animals. The chief species of trees so planted, all Asiatic, are *Butea frondosa*, *Schleichera trijuga*, *Ficus religiosa*, and *Zizyphus* spp.

Gum Resins

This is a small group of rather miscellaneous products. One of the best known is gamboge, from *Garcinia Morella*. From it is made a valuable pigment, and the name is a corruption of Cambodia, its country of origin.

Myrrh and bdellium are two closely related fragrant resins from species of *Balsamodendron* and *Commiphora*, inhabiting India, Arabia and Somaliland. They have long been familiar perfumes and are used for making toilet soaps and incense.

Asafoetida is also renowned for its scent but for a different reason. It comes from *Ferula* spp., chiefly from Persia, and is used in medicine. Ammoniacum and galbanum are from other members of the same family (that to which the carrot belongs), *Dorema Ammoniacum* and *Peucedanum galbanifluum* respectively, also from Persia and also used in medicine.

Balsams

Certain commodities of a more or less aromatic nature are called balsams and are described under that name here, but it is merely a designation of convenience and has no scientific meaning or significance.

The best known of them, especially to biology students, is Canada balsam, so important in microscopic work. It comes from the balsam fir (*Abies balsamea*), a native of Canada and the United States. Its value for mounting specimens is due to the fact that when hard it has a diffraction very like that of glass, so that there is the minimum dispersal of the light that passes through it. Oregon balsam is a similar product from *Pseudotsuga Douglasii*. Two others, also used in microscopy, are Venetian turpentine from the larch (*Larix europaea*) and Burgundy pitch from the spruce (*Picea excelsa*). The balsam exuding from the American spruce (*Picea alba*) is sometimes used as a rough and ready chewing gum.

Most of the balsams are of value in medicine. Balsam of

Copaiba from an American plant (*Copaifera Lansdorfii*), and benzoin from the Asiatic plant, *Styrax Benzoin*, are important and so are the balsam of Tolu and the balsam of Peru. Both these are from species of the genus *Myroxylon*, the former from *M. toluiferum* (South America) and the latter from *M. Pereirae* (Central America). These two and storax, a balsam from the west Asiatic tree *Liquidambar orientalis*, are wound secretions rather than normal products and are obtained by superficially injuring the plants. Other medicinal balsams are illurin balsam from *Daniella thurifera* (West Africa), gurjun balsam from species of *Dipterocarpus* (eastern Asia), scammony resin from the roots of *Convolvulus scammonia* (western Asia) and jalap resin from the roots of *Ipomoea Purga* (Mexico).

A few balsams are used in perfumery, as for instance the well-known frankincense or olibanum, which is the produce of *Boswellia Carteri* and *B. Frereana* from Somaliland. True opopanax is from a Greek plant *Opopanax Chironium*. Taca-mahac resin comes from several trees such as the American species *Protium pentaphyllum* and *Bursera tomentosa* and from the Asiatic plant *Calycophyllum inophyllum*. Ladanum, or gum-cistus, as it is sometimes called, is the gummy exuda-tion of species of *Cistus*, the genus to which the sun-roses of gardens belong, and especially of *C. ladaniferus* and *C. creticus*. These small shrubs occur very abundantly in many Mediter-ranean countries and the supply of resin comes chiefly thence. One method of collection used to be to drive sheep through the vegetation and then to recover the resin adhering to their wool. It is also said that goats are turned out to graze on the plants, so that in time their beards become soaked with the resin. The beards are then removed and the resin recovered. Ladanum must not be confused with laudanum, which is quite a different thing and comes from the opium poppy.

A rather special plant product that may be mentioned here is the true or Japanese lacquer. It comes from the stem of the lacquer tree, *Rhus vernicifera*. After purification it forms a high-quality and almost imperishable varnish.

Gums

The vegetable gums are not very many and most of them come from the genus *Acacia*. Of these gum-Arabic from various African and Asiatic species (principally *A. Senegal*), gum-Senegal, and Kordofan gum (from similar species) are the most important. Gum-tragacanth is obtained from *Astragalus gummifer* and other Asiatic species of this large genus, by wounding the stems.

A very important aromatic plant product allied to the resins and balsams is camphor, which is obtained by distilling the wood of the camphor laurel (*Cinnamomum Camphora*). The tree is native in parts of tropical Asia and is, or was, very abundant in Formosa, and to it that island owes much of its wealth. A similar product, Borneo camphor, comes from another Asiatic tree, *Dryobalanops aromatica*.

DYES AND TANS

Dyes

The vegetable dyes afford the second significant instance of plant products that have been supplanted by the synthetic products of the laboratory. A century ago man was still greatly dependent on plants for his colouring matters, but since then organic chemistry has developed so fast and so far that dyes of vegetable origin are now of secondary importance.

The largest class of vegetable dyes comprise those obtained from the wood of trees. Prominent among them is logwood or haematoxylin from the West Indian tree, *Haematoxylon campechianum*. Fustic, from the wood of the American tree *Chlorophora tinctoria*, is also important and so is red sandal wood (*Pterocarpus santalinus* and related spp.). Still others are camwood (*Baphia nitida*) from Africa, sappan (*Caesalpinia Sappan* and other spp.), young fustic from *Rhus Cotinus*, a native of Asia, and the wood of *Cladrastis tinctoria*.

In a few cases the whole plant yields a dye as in the indigo. This is one of the most important vegetable colours and comes from *Indigofera tinctoria*, and several others of the genus, mostly from Asia. The first extract of the plant is yellow, but on oxidation in air this changes to an intense blue. Similarly the whole plant of the dyer's weld (*Reseda lutea*), a plant indigenous to Europe, yields a dye.

Valuable root dyes are obtained from the alkannet (*Anchusa officinalis*) and from the true madder (*Rubia peregrina*) both natives of Europe and western Asia, the latter including Great Britain in its range. Two very familiar colours are the products of leaves. These are henna from the Asiatic *Lawsonia inermis*, and woad from the Eurasian *Isatis tinctoria*. The latter has been used since prehistoric times in our own country, and is still cultivated on a very small scale. The dye is obtained by pounding together the leaves and allowing them to ferment. Incidentally the knowledge that woad was the dye of the ancient Britons has led to the widespread and entirely erroneous idea that our pre-Roman ancestors were uncultured savages, an idea very wide of the mark, as the remains of their culture show. The very use of such a dye as woad indicates that their condition was far from being a primitive one.

The yellow dye turmeric is provided by the rhizomes of a tropical herb, *Curcuma longa*, a native of tropical Asia. In the East it has many uses, but in the West is chiefly familiar as giving the colour to the liquid in piccalilli.

The brilliant colours of flowers might be thought likely sources of vegetable dyes. One or two do indeed come from flowers, but they are not all chemically the substances which give the hues to petals. Such are the true saffron and the safflower. Both are European plants, the former being a crocus (*Crocus sativus*) and the latter a thistle-like plant (*Carthamus tinctorius*). In the first the dye comes from the brilliantly coloured yellow stigmas of the flower, in the latter a yellow dye is obtained from the whole florets. Rouge also is made from the safflower by powdering the florets and mixing them with talc. A yellow dye is also obtained from the flowers of the dyer's green weed (*Genista tinctoria*), a native of Europe, including Great Britain.

Seeds provide two well-known dyes, turkey-red from the Mediterranean plant *Peganum Harmala*, and annatto from the tropical tree *Bixa Orellana*; and a less familiar one from *Rhamnus infectoria* (southern Europe). The bark of certain other species of *Rhamnus* afford a green dye.

Finally we may mention the cactus, *Nopalea coccinellifera*. This is not itself a dye plant, but is the food of the cochineal insect and as such is widely grown in the tropics. It is a native of America, like almost all the other cacti.

Tans

Tans are rather complicated organic substances found abundantly in plants, and possessing two qualities which make them of industrial value. The first is that they give strongly coloured dark green or blue-black iron salts that can be used for inks and similar purposes, and the second is that they precipitate and render insoluble certain proteins. The latter is the real basis of their chief use in the tanning industry where they render the proteins in animal skins and hides innocuous and prevent them from decomposing. Tans for this use are all obtained from plants and mostly from the bark of trees.

The oaks furnish a very useful series of tans. The bark of the common oak, *Quercus Robur*, is extensively used in temperate countries and the galls or "oak-apples" of *Quercus infectoria*, as well as the young acorns of *Quercus Aegilops*, have a similar but more restricted use. Other tan-barks are obtained from the sweet chestnut (*Castanea sativa*) of southern Europe, from several species of the Australian *Eucalyptus* trees, under the name mallet-bark, from the North American loblolly bay (*Gordonia Lasianthus*), from the European larch (*Larix europaea*), from the Australian celery pine (*Phyllocladus trichomanoides*), from the Asiatic mangrove (*Rhizophora mucronata*), and from the North American hemlock spruce (*Tsuga canadensis*). The bark of the birch (*Betula* spp.) is used in the manufacture of Russian leather and helps to give it its characteristic smell. Oak bark, after it has been used in the tan-pits, is employed for covering the floors of riding schools and the surfaces of roads that traverse race courses.

Cutch is a tan from the wood of the Indian *Acacia Catechu*, and several Australian species of the same genus afford similar products. Another important tan is from the wood of the quebracho (*Schinopsis* spp.) from tropical America.

Several fruits also yield tans. Such are divi-divi pods (*Caesalpinia Coriaria*) from the West Indies, sant-pods (*Acacia arabica*) and the myrobalan (*Terminalia Chebula*) from Asia. Tans also come from the leaves of the sumach (*Rhus Coriaria*) from southern Europe, and from the roots of canaigre (*Rumex hymenosepalum*) of North America. Gambier is a tan product manufactured from a secretion of the Malayan tree, *Uncaria Gambier*.

FIBRES

Another great industrial group in which, with one major exception, plant products are the raw materials is that of the textile and fibre trades. The exception concerns the former alone, where animal products like wool are largely employed, and the latter are for all practical purposes vegetable only. The use of the words "textile and fibre" illustrates the two great classes into which fibrous vegetable products can be classified, namely spinning fibres and others, but this is an economic classification which rather cuts across the biological arrangement that is more convenient here.

From the commercial point of view a vegetable fibre may be defined as any portion of a plant body which is sufficiently strong and tensile to be woven or spliced. This definition would suggest that a great variety of plant structures are so used, and this is to some extent true, but by far the larger number of them are, morphologically, either seed hairs or fibrous sclerenchymatous cells. The first class is a very small one but this is compensated for by the almost supreme importance of one member of it, cotton, which alone is the basis of one of the greatest industries in the world. The second class is a much more heterogeneous one and includes all kinds of commodities, some of which would even strain the definition just given. The finer of these are used in textile work for lace and net-making; the rather coarser ones are employed for cordage and rope, and the coarsest are made into baskets, brooms and so on. Some furnish natural fabrics; others can be made into high grade paper; while still others can be utilised as stuffings and packings.

Cotton

Raw cotton consists of the white hairs that cover the seeds of several woody herbs belonging to the genus *Gossypium*, a group of plants distantly related to the hollyhock of gardens and to the wild mallows. These hairs are unicellular, and vary in length from $\frac{1}{2}$ to $2\frac{1}{2}$ inches. Commercially the hairs are referred to as "lint" and this is either "short-staple" or "long-staple" according to their length. Species of *Gossypium* are so widely spread through the tropics now that it is difficult to say exactly which species produce most of the cotton of commerce and of what countries they are or were once native. Much of the world's supply comes certainly from five species, but there are others as well. These five are *Gossypium herbaceum* and *G. arboreum*, generally known as the Asiatic cottons, and *G. hirsutum*, *G. barbadense* and *G. peruvianum*, the American cottons.

Cotton has been cultivated for hundreds of years. It was grown in Egypt and India very early in human history and many classical writers mention it, while early explorers to the New World found many evidences of its long-established use there too. In spite of this ancient history the pre-eminence of cotton as a textile material is really of comparatively recent origin, dating from about the middle of the nineteenth century. Up to that time its use on a large scale to replace wool was prevented by the difficulty of economically separating the hairs from the seeds, but about 1790 the first cotton "gin", capable of doing this expeditiously, was invented. About the same time machines for spinning were improved and new ones introduced (above all Hargreave's spinning jenny) and to complete the story, the utilisation of steam power followed almost immediately. The combined result of these developments was that the demand for cotton goods suddenly became enormous. Supplies had previously come almost entirely from India as a kind of side-line to the spice trade, but this source was soon inadequate and cotton growing spread widely, and in particular became established on a large scale in the southern United States (see Chapter IV).

This country has ever since remained the greatest producing region of the world, and to-day supplies more than half the whole world output. Next comes India, and then some distance behind, Egypt, Russia and China. The remainder comes mostly from other parts of America. Recently the crop has been introduced into central and warm-southern Africa, but the industry here is hardly yet established.

The uses of cotton are very numerous. First is its employment as a textile in the manufacture of fabrics. For this purpose the strength and peculiar twist of the hairs make it particularly suitable. The oldest and best-known cotton fabric is calico, a name of considerable historical interest because it is a corruption of Calicut, the first town in India visited by the Portuguese, in the fifteenth century. Gingham, muslin, casement-cloth, voile, chintz, cretonnes, dimity, velveteens, plush and corduroy are all made entirely or mostly from cotton, and it is used to a less extent in a number of others. Besides these it has several other uses such as for cotton-waste, cotton-wool, absorbent gauze, and sewing thread.

Other Vegetable Hairs

The seeds of many plants are covered with hairs, which aid in their dispersal, and repeated attempts have been made to use some of these in the same way as cotton but without notable success. Only one of them has a real commercial value. This is kapok, the seed hairs from an African tree, *Eriodendron*

anfractuosum. Even this is not used for spinning but for packing and stuffing lifebelts and other articles where its extreme
lightness, due to the inclusion of air among the hairs, is
valuable. The seed hairs of our native cotton grass (*Erio-
phorum* spp.) are similarly occasionally used for stuffing
pillows in country districts.

VEGETABLE FIBRES

These can be considered most easily if they are divided up into
groups according to their morphological nature. The first and
largest group contains the products derived from the fibrous
tissues in the stems of Dicotyledons. Such fibres are generally
found in or near the phloem, but a few are cortical. The second
group which is smaller, but still important, contain the fibres
from Monocotyledons. Sometimes they are from the stems,
but more often from the leaves and very occasionally from
the fruits. They all agree in being actually complete fibro-
vascular bundles, the important mechanical part being the
bundle sheaths. The texture of these bundle fibres varies very
much. The third group contains a number of miscellaneous
products of a fibrous nature which do not fall into either of the
other two categories.

Dicotyledonous Fibres

Flax, which comes from a herb of temperate countries, *Linum
usitatissimum,* well known for its beautiful blue flowers,
deserves first place here. It is the most delicate of all the true
fibres and the only one which can be used for weaving in the
same way as cotton. It grows fairly well in parts of the British
Isles, especially in Ireland with its moister climate, and until
the coming of cotton was of much greater importance than it
is now, because its main manufacture, linen, was almost without a rival. Ulster is now the centre of the British industry,
but Russia, Holland and India are the main producers of
the fibre. This is obtained from the plant by retting, a
process which consists of soaking the stems in water till they

are well rotted. A bacterial reaction plays a part in the loosening and separation of the tissues. The best linen is pure flax, and lawn and cambric (named from the French town Cambrai) are other flax fabrics. It is used, too, in the manufacture of twine, canvas and lace. The plant is also widely grown for linseed.

Jute is a rather coarser fibre used in the manufacture of rough fabrics such as packing-canvas and sacking, and also to a limited extent in rope-making. It comes from two species of large annual herbs native to India, *Corchorus capsularis* and *C. olitorius*. Like flax it is prepared by retting and is generally somewhat similar. Species of a related genus, *Triumfetta*, also yield fibre.

Another fibre similarly obtained is hemp, the product of a tall herb, *Cannabis sativa*, a native of eastern Europe and western Asia. It is used for sail-cloth, ropes and sacking and also for caulking seams in ships. Oakum, of sinister reputation, is the name given to hemp which has already been manufactured into rope. The hemp plant is also the source of the narcotic drug "hashish" or "bhang" which is much consumed in Asiatic countries.

Sunn hemp is a fibre rather like hemp, from another Asiatic plant, *Crotalaria juncea*, and many species of the tropical genera *Hibiscus* and *Abutilon*, which, like the cottons, belong to the mallow family, yield valuable stem fibres of a similar kind. Devil's cotton comes from *Abroma augusta* (India) and olona from *Touchardia latifolia* (Hawaii). Ramie or China grass (*Boehmeria nivea* var. *tenacissima*) is among the longest and toughest of all fibres, but is unfortunately rather difficult to prepare. Bass or bast, so much used for tying up plants in gardens, comes from the inner bark of lime trees or lindens (*Tilia* sp.). Similarly the inner bark of the paper mulberry (*Broussonetia papyrifera*) provides a fibre which is used by the natives of Polynesia for making tapa cloth. In other parts of the East paper is prepared from it. In Ceylon and Malay the upas (*Antiaris toxicaria*) also furnishes a substitute for cloth.

Monocotyledonous Fibres

The majority of these, including all the more important, are leaf fibres, a fact that is obviously associated with the narrow sword- or strap-shaped foliage of most Monocotyledons. They also afford yet another interesting comment on the value of scientific names, since most of them are known in English as forms of hemp or flax, whereas they are actually not related at all to those plants.

Manila hemp or abaca fibre, from the leaves of a species of banana, *Musa textilis*, is very important because it is especially suitable for making high-grade rope. When strength and quality are essential, as in mountaineering rope, Manila hemp is nearly always used. Old ropes of this material are sometimes made into paper. It is a native of, and chiefly cultivated in, the Philippines.

Sisal hemp from *Agave sisalana*, a plant native in tropical America, is similar but the product is not so well established in commerce. Of late years, however, its cultivation has much increased especially in the British Empire, and it will doubtless become more and more used. Another fibre, henequen, is prepared from *Agave fourcroydes*, and still other species are more or less valuable in the same way. The same plants yield large quantities of sap, from which the Mexican national drink "pulque" is made.

New Zealand hemp or flax, as it is alternatively called, is prepared from the leaves of *Phormium tenax*, a New Zealand plant belonging to the lily family. It is grown in many parts of the tropics, including the island of St Helena. In properties and uses it resembles the foregoing. Like it are several other fibres, such as Mauritius hemp from *Furcraea gigantea* (America), bowstring hemp from *Sansevieria zeylanica* (Asia), pineapple fibre from *Ananas* spp. (America), and the fibres from *Yucca filamentosa* (America) and *Pandanus utilis* (Old World).

Stem fibres are chiefly derived from the palms and are

generally very stout and scarcely fibrous in the accepted sense
of the word, as they tend to be brittle. They are used in fine
basket work, for mats and other similar objects. Palmyra fibre
comes from the palmyra palm (*Borassus flabellifer*), native to
and cultivated in the Old World tropics, piassaba fibre from
the American palms, *Attalea funifera* and *Leopoldinia Piassaba*,
and Kitul fibre from *Caryota urens* (Ceylon). Raffia, familiar
in plaited handicrafts, is another palm product from *Raphia
Ruffia*, the African wine palm. A stem fibre also comes from
certain species of *Tillandsia* (America), a genus of the pineapple family.

Coir is the only fruit fibre we need mention. It is the fibrous
outer husk and pericarp of the coconut, and is yet another
example of the value of that plant. It is used for matting,
brooms and brushes. Matting for cricket pitches is generally
made from coir.

Miscellaneous Fibre Products

The stems of several Monocotyledonous plants are used for
making special grades of paper. The fibres are not separated
from the stems, but the value of the latter depends upon the
presence of the former, and they may therefore be considered
fibre products.

Straw, the ripened and dead stems of most of the common
cereals, can be used for this purpose, but several other plants
are particularly valuable. The Egyptian papyrus (*Cyperus
Papyrus*) is one of the best known, and esparto grass from
Stipa tenacissima, of Mediterranean countries, is also fairly
familiar. A very common rush, *Juncus effusus*, is sometimes
used in the same way in Japan. The cord grass (*Spartina
Townsendii*) which, since the beginning of the century, has
become established in great quantities in parts of southern
England, has been exploited in the same way. Paper made
from it was of some value in war time but does not compete
with the ordinary kinds normally.

The leaves of the palmetto palm (*Sabal Palmetto*) from

tropical America are used for thatching, and the straw of the common reed (*Phragmites communis*) is similarly used, together with ordinary straw, in temperate regions.

Rattans are the strong and fibrous stems of climbing palms belonging chiefly to the genus *Calamus*, natives of tropical Asia. They lend themselves to the making of walking-sticks and canes.

Panama hats hardly strike one as important plant commodities but in fact the best are made exclusively from the young leaves of a particular small American plant (*Carludovica palmata*), which has a considerable value on that account.

The lace-bark tree of the West Indies (*Lagetta lintearia*) is more a botanical curiosity than anything else. The fibrous bark separates easily into a number of concentric layers, each of which forms an open network, and these are occasionally used in native costumery.

Another unusual fibre product is the sponge cucumber or bath loofah (*Luffa cylindrica*) which consists of the fibrous skeleton of the vegetable marrow-like fruit.

The long narrow leaves of *Zostera marina*, the eel grass, one of the few marine Angiosperms, are sometimes used as a sound-absorbing packing for walls and partitions.

MAP 6

SOUTH AMERICA

SOUTH AMERICA

Chapter XI

ALCOHOL: DRUGS: FODDERS: MISCELLANEOUS

ALCOHOL

Invaluable as the carbohydrates are in providing us directly with one of the most important food supplies, they also furnish indirectly another series of products which may or may not, according to fancy, be ranked almost with the foods in value. These are the various alcoholic liquids obtained by the fermentation of sugars and starches.

A great many attempts have been made to produce alcohol synthetically on a commercial scale, but up to the present they have not been very successful and all the alcohol of commerce actually comes from carbohydrates, originally produced by plants.

Two great classes of carbohydrates are used, the sugars and starches and the celluloses. Almost any kind of starch will suffice, but the sources naturally exploited are the cereals and the potato. In the tropics cassava and arrowroot are also used. Similarly almost any sugary juice can be employed and choice merely falls on those most easily obtainable. It is for this reason that so many countries have their own peculiar sources of alcoholic beverages from plant juices which are not plentiful enough to be of commercial value, but which are quite adequate for local needs. Production of alcohol from celluloses and similar bodies is more complicated, but materials like wood waste, that are otherwise valueless, can be used.

In all cases the actual production of alcohol depends on two processes, first the conversion of the complex carbohydrates into sugars and secondly the fermentation of these. In nature certain very simple fungi, the yeasts, perform these two actions by means of the enzymes that they secrete, that concerned in the first being diastase and that in the second zymase. Sometimes however, as in the celluloses, the carbohydrates cannot be broken down by enzyme action but have to be hydrolysed chemically. The essential point is to obtain a solution of simple sugars.

The general methods of alcohol production may be exemplified by referring to the manufacture of some of the commoner alcoholic beverages.

Beer is made from barley. The grain is allowed to germinate, so that the enzymes reach a maximum activity and the reserve carbohydrates are converted into sugars. This malt, as it is called, is then killed and mashed and a sugary solution called wort is extracted from it. Yeast is added to the wort and the sugar or some of it is converted into alcohol. The result is a dilute aqueous alcoholic solution, which is finally flavoured with hops and other ingredients. Cider and perry are similar, except that the wort is the juice expressed from apples and pears respectively. In all these drinks the percentage of alcohol is low because the wort is only a dilute solution of sugar.

Wine is obtained in like manner from the juice of the grape, but differs markedly in that yeast is not deliberately added, the sugar solution being fermented by wild yeasts which live naturally on the grapes. Various chemical substances are concerned in the finer details of wine making and give the different flavours. In "still" wines the fermentation is complete before the liquid is bottled; in "sparkling" wines the last stages of fermentation take place in the bottle, so that a quantity of gas is liberated when it is opened.

Spirits are obtained by the distillation of wines and beers and hence contain more concentrated solutions of alcohol. Broadly speaking, brandies are distilled from wines, and whiskies and gins from malt liquors. Rum is similarly obtained from molasses. Liqueurs are, for the most part, spirits flavoured with various essential oils such as have already been described.

Among the best-known exotic alcoholic drinks are the Mexican pulque (and its spirit mescal) from species of *Agave*, the Japanese saki from rice, and toddy-wine from various kinds of palms.

DRUGS

The subject of vegetable drugs is much too vast to be dealt with here at any length, and any detailed account of them must be sought in books especially concerning them. Here it is possible only to describe a few of the most important and to give a list of certain others.

One plant product which must on all counts rank as a drug occupies a position in commerce and human affairs generally quite unlike any other and comes nearest of all such products to food. This is tobacco, yet another of the great plant gifts of the New World to the Old.

There are many familiar stories of the introduction of tobacco into England about 1560, and with them Sir Walter Ralegh's name is always associated. There is no doubt that he was at least one of the first Englishmen to smoke tobacco, but it is probable that the introduction of the plant was due more to Mr Ralph Lane, who was the Governor of Virginia at the time. At all events, once in Europe it quickly spread and the countries round the Mediterranean became the centre of the Old World cultivation. Hence came the cigarette, whose centenary has just been observed.

The tobacco of commerce is almost entirely the produce of three species of the genus *Nicotiana*, *N. Tabacum*, *N. rustica* and *N. persica*. All three are natives of America but nowadays their cultivation is rather segregated. The first is grown chiefly in America, the second produces Turkish tobacco, mostly for cigarettes, and the third is grown chiefly in Persia for use in hookahs. The plants are annual and the commercial product is prepared by drying the leaves, either by sun or artificially, and then slightly fermenting them by bacterial action. It is this fermentation that gives tobacco its valuable flavour. There are also present minute quantities of the alkaloid nicotine. Tobacco is generally smoked but is also chewed and, when powdered, forms snuff. It is smoked in cigars, pipes and cigarettes. The cigar is the most luxurious smoke and is most popular in warm countries and especially where tobacco is grown. Pipe-smoking is characteristic of the peoples of the North temperate regions, as, for instance, the North American Indians. Cigarettes are the most recent adaptation.

Tobacco is grown to-day in many warm countries where the mean temperature does not fall below 40 and where frosts do not occur, but North America still produces the largest part of the world's supply, especially of pipe tobacco. The other important producing countries are parts of Malay, Bulgaria and Turkey. Its cultivation is now spreading in the British Empire, and empire tobaccos are beginning to compete with Virginian brands. In good seasons the crop can be grown in the south of England, but not on a commercial basis.

It is convenient here to mention a particular plant product which, although not related to tobacco, is a drug and employed largely in the East in rather similar ways for chewing. This is the betel nut, the seed of a palm (*Areca Catechu*). The seed is cut up and mixed with lime and wrapped in the leaves of the betel pepper (*Piper Betle*). It is said to aid digestion.

From the earliest times the value of plants as a source of medicinal drugs has ranked next to their importance as sources of food. Their value in this way has tended to diminish with the gradual development of organic chemistry, but even to-day we are still dependent upon plants for many of the most important medicines. The number of plants which have at one time or another been considered efficacious in disease and sickness is legion and, indeed, almost every easily available plant has enjoyed some reputation in this way. Most of them, however, have now passed out of use either because increased investigation has shown them to be valueless, or because they have been supplanted by synthetic compounds, and to-day the number of plant drugs in general use is comparatively limited. Even so the number is too great to permit of their mention here, and it is necessary to restrict our consideration to those of outstanding merit.

In deciding which these are there are two books which are our guides. These are the *British Pharmacopeia*, of which a new edition appeared in 1932, and the *British Pharmaceutical Codex*. The former may be described as a standard catalogue of all the medicinal remedies that are to be considered as of established and undisputed value by those most qualified to give an opinion. It is published with Government Authority by the General Medical Council, and is the ultimate referee on all matters relating to the dispensing of medicines. As a reflection of this the remedies in it are called "official". The *Codex* is a much larger book containing the substance of the *British Pharmacopeia* but also a great many additional remedies, which although valuable are perhaps of less merit than those in the *Pharmacopeia*. Both books are used in dispensing, and the difference between them is simply a matter of standards.

For our present purposes we must confine ourselves to a short account of the vegetable drugs in the *British Pharmacopeia*, but information about the others can easily be obtained from the *Codex*. We must also restrict ourselves to drugs which, unlike some of the balsams, have not already been mentioned.

Most drugs, like fire, are good servants but bad masters, and may be harmful or beneficial according to the way in which they are used. In most the balance is well on the credit side of the sheet, but in a few the opposite is the case. Among these opium stands out as one of the most baneful plant products despite its undoubted and great medicinal value. The raw product consists of the dried and compressed latex from the unripe fruits of the opium poppy (*Papaver somniferum*), a native of western Asia. This contains several highly prized narcotic alkaloids (a class of chemical substances very common in plants, and affording the active principles of many drugs), which when separated afford the drugs morphine, codeine, thebaine and narcotine, and these have great uses when employed under skilled supervision. Unfortunately their narcotic and soothing effects can also be felt when the opium is smoked like tobacco. At first the ill-effects are not marked, but opium smoking easily becomes a habit which can only be broken with difficulty, and continued indulgence has extremely serious effects, both physical and moral, and may finally end in death.

The story of opium and the opium trade is especially the story of China, although the drug was not introduced into that country till the seventeenth century, and has only been grown there for one hundred years or so. Before then China received most of her supplies from India. The story of the opium trade with China is a long one and cannot be told here, but essentially it is the story of the struggle of the Chinese governments to prevent the pouring of opium into their country by British firms operating from India. The length of this struggle, now successfully concluded, and its far-reaching reverberations, form one of the least pleasant chapters in the history of the British Empire in the East.

Unlike opium, quinine has never been anything but the greatest boon to man. It is a preventive of, and a remedy for, many fevers, especially malaria, and as such is not only a most important medicine but has also played a leading part in making possible the colonisation of many parts of the tropics by white people. Probably no one drug has done so much for the alleviation of the pains of the human race. It is obtained from the bark of several species of the genus *Cinchona*, particularly *C. succirubra*, all natives of tropical America, but it is now chiefly produced in India where its cultivation was established nearly a century ago, mainly by the interest and influence of Lady Canning when her husband was Viceroy. An old name for it is "Jesuit's Bark", a name which associates it with the early missionaries in South America. It is said that its efficacy was discovered from the health-giving qualities of the water of a pool into which some of the branches of the tree had fallen.

Several members of the potato family are important drug

plants, because of the alkaloids they contain. Among them are the deadly nightshade (*Atropa Belladonna*) which gives atropine and belladonna, the thorn apple (*Datura Stramonium*) which gives stramonium, and the henbane (*Hyoscyamus niger*) from which comes hyoscyamine. All these are natives of Europe.

Two rather similar drugs are cocaine, obtained from the leaves of the coca tree (*Erythroxylon Coca*), of tropical America, and strychnine from the seeds of *Strychnos Nux-vomica*, a tree native to India and Ceylon.

Several important drugs are specially familiar to us in the early years of our lives. Dill comes from *Anethum graveolens* (west Asia), aloes from several species of the genus *Aloe* from Africa, ipecacuanha from the root of *Cephaëlis Ipecacuanha* (Brazil), rhubarb from the rhizomes of *Rheum palmatum* and other related species chiefly from China and Tibet, and senna from the leaflets and pods of *Cassia acutifolia* and *C. angustifolia*, both Asiatic species.

Other valued and familiar drugs are aconite from the European monkshood (*Aconitum Napellus*), cascara sagrada from the dried bark of *Rhamnus Purshiana* (North America), colocynth from the dried fruit-pulp of the colocynth (*Citrullus Colocynthis*) of the Old World, digitalis from the leaf of the foxglove (*Digitalis purpurea*), gentian from the root of the yellow gentian of central Europe (*Gentiana lutea*), liquorice, also eaten as a sweetmeat, from the rhizome of *Glycyrrhiza glabra* (Europe), squill from the bulb of *Urginea Scilla* (Eurasia), and valerian from the rhizome and roots of the European herb, *Valeriana officinalis*.

Less familiar drug plants in the *British Pharmacopeia* are buchu, the dried leaves of the South African plant *Barosma betulina*, calumba root from *Jateorhiza palmata* (Africa), chrysarobin, a deposit in the trunks of the tree *Andira Araroba*, cassia from the pods of *Cassia fistula*, colchicum from the corm and seeds of the European meadow saffron (*Colchicum officinale*), hamamelis from the leaves of the North American witch-hazel (*Hamamelis virginiana*), jalap root from species of *Ipomoea*, krameria from the root of *Krameria triandra* (tropical America), lobelia from the North American herb, *Lobelia inflata*, pilocarpine or jaborandi from *Pilocarpus microphyllus* (tropical America), cherry bark from the North American wild cherry (*Prunus serotina*), quassia bark from *Quassia amara* (tropical America), quillaja bark from *Quillaja Saponaria* (South America), santonin from the Asiatic herb *Artemisia Cina*, salicin from the bark of various species of willow (*Salix* spp.), senega from the roots of *Polygala Senega* (North America), and strophanthus from the seeds of several species of the African genus *Strophanthus*.

FODDERS AND MISCELLANEOUS

The necessarily long earlier account of the human vegetable foods tends rather to obscure the fact that a great deal of agricultural practice is concerned primarily not with providing food for man directly, but in providing food for animals which may in turn furnish nourishment for the human race. Two other reasons also make it a little difficult to realise how large a part is ultimately played in human economy by fodders: most such plants are consumed where they are grown, and therefore do not become articles of trade; and the horse, which in years past was the most conspicuous fodder animal to the ordinary man in the street, is becoming more and more scarce, particularly in towns.

Fodders and feeding-stuffs generally differ from human foods in the notable particular that they are bulky and that their nourishment is not very concentrated. They are indeed mostly foliage and therefore resemble the green vegetables that we ourselves eat, and like them contain very large quantities of water. A grazing animal has therefore to consume a large amount of food and to spend a great proportion of its time doing so.

If we compare human diets with those of ordinary stock animals we notice a very conspicuous difference between them. We take our food almost entirely in concentrated forms like cereals and meat, and make very little real use of succulent plant tissues for the major constituents of our diet. Stock, on the other hand, lives almost equally exclusively on foliage and other succulent tissues, which contain great amounts of water, and takes very little dry or concentrated food, and that only when artificially supplied. This difference is not entirely one of the development of human preferences but is indicative of a fundamental difference in the processes of digestion. The human alimentary canal with its comparatively simple stomach is capable of dealing with concentrated foods, but that of herbivorous animals, with its complicated and successive stomachs, of dealing with the reverse kind of nutriment. Nevertheless stock animals require proportionately just as much fuel and building materials for the maintenance of their bodily activities as we do. The result is that the diet of most grazing animals is much more bulky than that of human beings and takes very much longer to consume, and such animals normally spend a great part of their life in eating.

This difference in physiology has also, from the point of view of agriculture, another important aspect. Grazing animals, in order to obtain the necessary quantities of nourishment, are normally obliged to consume a good deal of material which is relatively indigestible and which passes through the body unabsorbed. It is, however, in the process more or less broken down and changed, and when finally deposited is of considerable value as manure. In fact so valuable is it that an appreciable proportion of the cost of the original material is generally considered to be recovered in this way, and the natural manuring of land by allowing stock to graze over it is a very definite aspect of agricultural practice.

During summer, when pasture is fresh and abundant, most stock can be adequately fed simply by turning it out to grass, but in winter when grass growth ceases and annual crops die down it is generally necessary to augment supplies by other means such as preserved, and usually dry, fodder, or by artificial products. The provision of these is a characteristic feature of modern stock farming and has a very marked effect upon human food supplies. Before the provision of winter feed became easily possible it was only with considerable difficulty that animals could be maintained over the winter, and it was the general practice to slaughter a great deal of the barren stock at the end of the summer. As a result fresh animal food, especially meat, was rarely to be obtained in the winter and its place had to be taken by supplies preserved by salting or curing. This was not only monotonous but in some ways definitely injurious to health, since the methods of preservation or lack of variety tended to result in the absence of essential nutritive substances such as certain of the vitamins.

At the same time dry and artificial fodder is used not only to tide stock over the winter but also to enable greater numbers of animals to be maintained than could support themselves simply on the vegetation of the land that they occupy.

It will be seen from these remarks that fodders are actually of three kinds: fresh growing crops usually consumed as such without harvesting; crops which can be stored and drawn upon as desired after harvesting; and artificial manufactured fodders.

The first kind can hardly be considered fully here, because there are so many of them, and because every country has its own particular sorts. They do, however, fall mainly into two great groups, the grasses and the clovers, using the latter word in a very wide sense. Enough has already been said at the beginning of Chapter VI of the part that grasses play and have played in human history, but it is important in this connection to remember that even before they were exploited as cereals these plants were the basis of the earliest animal farming, and the fundamental factor in nomadic civilisation. The clovers are rather different because they rarely occur naturally in sufficient quantity to provide appreciable amounts of animal food. On the other hand, they contribute largely to the bulk of the deliberately sown and grown fresh fodders (grasses also are of course sown when necessary). As with the grasses many species are used for the purpose, but those of temperate regions and especially of our own country are mostly members of the clover genus proper (*Trifolium* spp.), the medicks and lucernes (*Medicago* spp.), and the vetches (*Vicia* spp.). Sainfoin (*Onobrychis sativa*) and melilot (*Melilotus* spp.) are also valuable. The grasses have rather complementary advantages. These are for the most part perennial, providing constant supplies and requiring little or no attention. The clovers are mostly annuals and require cultivation, but provide particularly suitable food combinations and, at the same time, improve the soil by bacterial action in a way that has already been described.

Fodders of the second class are of three kinds: dead stems and foliage, roots, and seeds and fruits. Commercially hay and straw are by far the most important of the first kind. Hay consists of the herbage, mostly grasses, of rich pasture land, cut early in summer when it is at its freshest and subsequently dried by the aid of the sun. It varies enormously in content and value. Almost any pasture sufficiently thick to repay the labour of cutting can be made to yield a crop of hay, but the best is obtained from meadows where a system of irrigation is practised. This water-meadow farming is a characteristic feature of parts of southern England. The preservation of hay depends chiefly on the prevention of bacterial decay by rapid drying, in the course of which so much water is lost that the product is no longer a suitable medium for the growth of bacteria. Of late years another method of keeping green crops over the winter has been developed to some extent. It is called ensilage and consists of building up the fresh-cut crops into heaps and covering them with soil or in packing them into trenches or other specially built receptacles. The important points to be observed are maintenance of pressure and exclusion of air. Materials so treated undergo a modified bacterial fermentation. They remain fairly juicy, but there is a good deal of chemical change and it is doubtful whether the product has the same nutritive value as sun-dried hay. Ensilage has not become popular in England, perhaps because there is no real need for it.

Straw is a general name given to the dry stalks of grasses, but usually applied specifically to those of the cultivated cereals left after the grain has been harvested. All the ordinary cereals yield straw, but there is a good deal of difference between the various sorts. Wheat straw is the most valuable and, in the East, rice straw has many uses. In agriculture straw is used chiefly as litter and bedding although it is to some extent edible, but it is mostly employed in ways quite remote from fodder, as in the making of cardboard, hats and such-like articles. In former times it was used much for thatching. For this purpose reed straw is the best material, but this is nowadays usually replaced by wheat straw.

The common root crops like turnips and swedes are biennials and accumulate in their roots during the first growing season material used in the second season for the great biological effort of flowering. The roots are therefore at their maximum size at the end of the first summer, and they will retain this condition without noticeable shrinkage until the next season, that is to say, during the winter. They therefore provide an admirable winter feed and are as such widely grown. So general is their use now that it is difficult to realise that their cultivation for this purpose was introduced into England not more than two centuries ago. Various kinds are used but the commonest are turnips and swedes (*Brassica* spp.) and beets and mangold wurzels (*Beta* spp.).

The seeds and fruits used for feeding stock are for obvious reasons generally among those also used for human foods, except that the less choice kinds are commonly employed. Many cereals, for instance, are used, but commercially at any rate, maize and oats, which are on the whole of least human value, are the most important. A great deal of maize in particular is consumed in this way, especially as poultry food. A few pulses are also used and buckwheat is important. Another plant product falling under this head and not previously mentioned is the carob. Carobs are the dried pods of the locust tree (*Ceratonia siliqua*), a native of the Mediterranean regions. The seeds and the pulp of the pods are rich in sugar and the whole provides a valuable food for pigs and cattle. The carat, familiar as a jeweller's weight, is derived from the seeds of this plant, which were formerly used as weights in Arabia.

Regarding artificially manufactured fodder, little need be said here beyond referring the reader back to the paragraphs on oils and fats. Nearly all such fodders are comprised under the heading of oil-cake and this is made, as has been described, from the remnants of a great many seeds and fruits after the bulk of the oil that they contain has been extracted or expressed.

FLOWERS, SEEDS AND BULBS

The last kind of flowering-plant product to be described is that of plants grown not for their food or as raw materials but for their beauty, and includes the trade in cut flowers and in seeds and bulbs intended purely for horticultural or indoor use.

Most cut flowers have necessarily to be sold within easy reach of their place of production, because they are unsuited for long and rough transport, but a great many kinds will travel fairly well with due care in packing. Flower-growing for the ordinary market is generally run as a kind of side-line to market gardening, but in some parts of the world it is a trade entirely by itself. Great Britain, for instance, receives considerable supplies of the less tender kinds during the winter from southern Europe, and in early spring comes the flower harvest of its own more favoured spots like the Scilly Islands. Similarly in other parts of the world cut flowers often form a minor source of trade, and even if the total intrinsic value is small this particular branch of plant economics must not be forgotten.

The provision and supply of the reproductive parts of plants for the stocking of gardens and for indoor uses is a more important industry. Here again the plants generally required in any particular country are usually those easily grown therein, and trade in growing plants and their seeds does not usually reach international dimensions. It is rather different, however, in the case of bulbs, chiefly because up to now the whole world trade has tended to be centred in Holland. This country has long been the centre of bulb production, partly because the nature and organisation of the land there and intensive methods of cultivation are appropriate to it, but this does not altogether explain the association.

The Dutch industry really commenced with the introduction into the country of the tulip (*Tulipa Gesneriana*) from western Asia about 1600. This apparently unimportant event had far-reaching consequences and is one of the most curious episodes in European history. Almost at once the plant began to exercise an almost incredible fascination over the people and attained a popularity which more or less justifies the name of "Tulip mania" which is sometimes given to it. This was at its height in the early part of the seventeenth century (see Dumas, *The Black Tulip*), and at that time almost the whole energies of the country were devoted to the cultivation of the plant and the production of new colours and forms. Immense sums were given for rare or unique bulbs, and fortunes were quickly made and lost. Finally the craze diminished, but Holland has remained ever since a leading country in bulb production.

In the last few years successful attempts have been made to establish bulb cultivation in that part of Lincolnshire appropriately enough called Holland, and to-day this region is the centre of a flourishing, if small, industry which will doubtless expand further. In the spring it also supplies considerable quantities of cut flowers.

In concluding this short notice of the industries concerning living plants we may conveniently consider one other use of plants so unlike the rest that it scarcely falls into any category or scheme of classification. This is the employment of living plants for the purposes of consolidating soils or of protecting other crops. The former is mostly seen in sea-side planting where it is desirable to arrest the progress of erosion or to bind and immobilise shifting sand. In different parts of the world a number of plants is used for this purpose, but in Britain those mostly concerned are such seaside grasses as the marram (*Psamma arenaria*) and the lyme grass (*Elymus arenarius*). The sea buckthorn (*Hippophaë rhamnoides*), a spiny shrub of a few feet in height, and the tamarisk (*Tamarix gallica*) are also sometimes employed, although they have not the actual binding power of the grasses. In the south of England there is illustrated another similar but minor use of plants in the planting, on bare cliff slopes, of a species of *Mesembryan-themum*, a fleshy leaved plant with purple flowers superficially resembling a daisy capitulum. In tropical regions species of *Casuarina* and *Hibiscus* are planted on beaches.

Plants as protective agencies are of most use either against wind or as providing shade for other plants. Windbreaks, such as can be made by growing plants which are resistant to wind, are in certain parts of the world very important and the species used in them depend much on the part of the world concerned. Oranges, for instance, are very susceptible to wind, and citrus orchards are therefore commonly surrounded by belts of bushes or trees which serve to intercept the wind. The plants so used must be fast growers, resistant themselves to wind and able to stand severe pruning and shaping. Among the kinds commonly used are species of *Eucalyptus* and *Eugenia*, and various shrubby members of the Leguminosae-like species of *Caragana* and *Tephrosia*. If the plant so used itself also produces a crop of some sort, so much the better.

Windbreaks of a sort are not unknown in Britain and two instances may be given. The first is the use of high hedges, often of beech or holly, to protect such crops as hops which are liable to be seriously disarranged by sudden wind. The second is the planting of trees on the exposed sides of farms and farm-yards. It is not uncommon on the Yorkshire wolds, where the winters tend to be severe, to see farm buildings surrounded by trees on the north, west and east.

The other outstanding example of the use of one crop to protect another is afforded by the plant known popularly as the "mother of cocoa" (*Gliricidia sepium*), which is normally planted in young cocoa plantations. It grows faster than the cocoa trees and serves as a protection for them against excessive insolation during their early years. A similar method is sometimes employed with other crops.

Chapter XII

THE USEFUL PRODUCTS OF THE LOWER PLANTS: AND CONCLUDING NOTES ON VEGETABLE PRODUCTS

The Lower Plants, or Cryptogams, to give them their more accurate and scientific name, afford a fair number of useful products, but none of them is of very great importance compared with most of those we have described among the seed plants.

The members of the great group of the bacteria are, as has been described in Chapter v, of vital significance in the general economy of nature, but these plants enter commerce scarcely at all. At the same time many of them are of great value as a source of the vaccines and anti-toxins used in medicine, and this alone must place the bacteria high in the list of plants of service to man.

The fungi are more conspicuously useful and indeed furnish in their edible sorts the most familiar of the commodities derived from Cryptogams. A great many of the larger kinds can be eaten and the fact that only the mushroom (*Psalliota campestris*) is commonly consumed in our own country merely indicates our national conservatism in matters of diet. It is true that the truffles (*Tuber* spp.) and the morel (*Morchella esculenta*) are used to a small extent, but many excellent kinds are quite neglected. In most other European countries a much larger variety is utilised and the lists of officially edible species are long. In France for instance the public sale of at least thirty species is permitted.

Among the simpler kinds of fungi the yeasts and certain other related species are of considerable value in virtue of the chemical reactions carried on by the enzymes they contain.

The use of yeasts in alcoholic fermentation has been mentioned already, but another similar, though less familiar application, is that of the vinegar fungus (*Mycoderma aceti*), which converts alcohol into acetic acid.

The poisonous properties of the fungi are well known and it is not surprising that several kinds have a value in medicine. In different parts of the world many are used in this way but at present only one remains in the *British Pharmacopeia*. This is the ergot (*Claviceps purpurea*), which is parasitic on grasses, and the drug consists of the sclerotia of the fungus formed in the fruiting ears of the grain. The chief active principle of ergot is the alkaloid ergotoxine.

Several other fungi have limited uses of a rather local importance and *Chlorosplenium aeruginosum* is a specially peculiar one. This is a saprophytic fungus living in decayed wood. One of the effects of its presence is to give to the wood that it infects a striking metallic green colour, and wood so coloured is used in the manufacture of sundry small articles that go by the name of Tunbridge ware.

The lichens, which are plants consisting of a fungus and an alga living together symbiotically, afford various minor useful products. A very few like *Cetraria islandica* are eaten. The reindeer moss (*Cladonia rangifera*) is also of first-rate importance in furnishing food for the reindeer herds in the arctic tundras.

Apart from food, the lichens also furnish certain dyes. Litmus is such a colouring matter from *Roccella tinctoria*, *Lecanora tartarica* and others, and some species yield lichen acids which, when treated with alkaline mordants, give yellow and brown dyes. Harris tweeds, the making of which is a cottage industry, are usually coloured by means of these substances.

The useful members of the algae all belong to the predominant marine forms, and these sea-weeds have a considerable variety of uses which make them almost certainly the most important members of the Cryptogams in this respect.

First and foremost is their value as sources of the elements iodine and potassium and of their salts. These are usually obtained from "kelp", which is the ash derived by burning certain of the larger brown sea-weeds, and especially those of the genera *Laminaria* and *Fucus*. Most exposed temperate coasts are rich in these plants, but the kelp industry is mainly centred on the two sides of the north Pacific Ocean. The presence of the elements mentioned makes the plants useful not only as a direct source of them but also less directly as manures. Sea-weeds are widely used for this purpose, but unless previously treated in certain chemical ways are very slow in disintegrating and liberating their contents.

A number of kinds of sea-weeds can be used as food. In Japan especially several are used in this way but in Britain only three—the carageen or Irish moss (*Chondrus crispus*), laver (*Porphyra laciniata*) and dulse (*Iridaea edulis*)—are at all commonly consumed. Their value lies in their copious mucilage, which is of a carbohydrate nature, and even if they are not eaten directly this can be used in other ways, such as making jellies and blancmanges. A peculiar example of the use of sea-weed mucilage is in the manufacture of agar-agar, made from species of the genus *Gelidium*. This is a jelly particularly used as a basis of the nutritive media on which the bacteria and fungi are cultured in laboratories.

These mucilages are also used in certain industrial processes such as the sizing of cloth, and they have been suggested as a source of the sugar mannite. An organic acid occurring in sea-weeds can be manufactured into a product capable of being used as a substitute for horn and as an insulator.

The higher Cryptogams, comprising the Bryophytes and Pteridophytes, afford, compared with the Thallophytes, very few products and these only of a minor kind. The Bryophytes especially are practically useless, and the only exception to this statement that comes readily to mind is the employment of some of the bog-mosses (*Sphagnum* spp.) as absorptive agencies in surgical dressings.

The Pteridophytes (Ferns and their allies) are also relatively useless. The rhizomes and other parts of the male fern (*Lastrea Filix-mas*) are official drugs, and the spores of the club-mosses (*Lycopodium* spp.) furnish a very fine powder, also used in medicine. One or two of the tree ferns like *Cibotium Chamissoi*, from Hawaii, contain much starch and are very occasionally used as a source of farinaceous food. The common bracken (*Pteridium aquilinum*) is frequently cut and dried and used as litter or for temporary thatching. Almost the only other useful members of the group are the horsetails (*Equisetum* spp.). The stems of these plants contain a good deal of silica and are for this reason sometimes used as abrasives. Such are the limited uses of living Pteridophytes but, in contrast, it must be remembered that the innumerable members of the group that lived in past ages have left us an invaluable legacy in the form of coal.

So ends the story of the exploitation of plants by man—an exploitation which has become an essential preliminary to his existence. It is rather natural to enquire—"How complete is this exploitation? Are there still more useful plants to be discovered?" The answer is twofold. The discovery of an entirely new plant of first-class economic importance is unlikely and becoming more unlikely every day. Few parts of the world remain now unexplored, and it is improbable that any considerable number of plants, markedly unlike those we know already, that is to say, belonging to new or very rare families, remain to be found. There *may* be something startling but it is not probable. On the other hand, it is quite certain that we have not made full use of the plants which we know already. Let us consider the position.

We have mentioned something like 600 plant species in the course of this book and, without any claim to absolute completeness, this number certainly represents all those which have any intrinsic value in world commerce. Yet the total number of wild species of flowering plants is probably about 250,000. Actually if we consider the number of plant products of really first-rate importance the number of species concerned is under one hundred, and incidentally it will be noticed how often more than one product is obtained from the same species. The position therefore seems to be that by exploiting these comparatively few species they can be made to yield, or at least have so far been made to yield, all that the human race requires from the plant world. But this is not to say that no others can be used, and the future development of economic botany will certainly be considerably concerned with the bringing into commerce of additional species not now used to any extent. It is natural enough to take the line of least resistance and, while the product of one species suffices, there is little inducement to worry about others. This was strikingly illustrated during the War. Then, when normal supplies were all too often interrupted, all kinds of plants usually quite ignored were pressed into service. There is a very interesting book by an Italian (Bruttini) dealing with this subject. In it he describes all these uncommon uses of familiar plants and gives most impressive lists of those capable, when the need sufficiently arises, of giving us useful products. They form, as it were, a reserve for future use.

Naturally enough they are not so valuable as those in more ordinary employment simply because, for the most part, they have never been improved. In this connection it is very interesting to note that almost all the main crop plants have been known and grown for a very long time. The only exception to this is the case of certain New World crops which, as far as the East is concerned, are comparatively recent, but these have all been of very long-standing cultivation in their own countries.

In short, it would seem that man very early in his history exploited the cream of the world's useful plants, and that they have sufficed him ever since. The future may well see fresh species brought into use, but these are likely to be closely related to those already familiar, except perhaps in the tropics where there is special room for the growth of agriculture and the exploitation of new crops.

Chapter XIII

THE ECONOMIC BOTANY OF GREAT BRITAIN

So far the object of this book has been to draw a perfectly general picture of the plant kingdom in its relation to the human communities of the world without referring specially to any one people. Such a broad treatment has the disadvantage that it necessitates talking in generalities, and generalities are apt to be vague and colourless. Let us, therefore, in this final chapter, try to give point to much that has been said previously by describing the part that considerations of economic botany have played, and still play, in influencing the social and economic structure of a single nation.

It would naturally be convenient to take as our example the country with which the majority of those who read this book are most likely to be familiar, namely Great Britain, but there are other reasons which make this choice particularly suitable. Great Britain, by which is meant England, Wales and Scotland, is in the combination of three respects unique among the countries of the world. In the first place it is an island and a comparatively small one at that. In the second it has a density of population greater than that of any other leading power, and except for Belgium, greater than that of any other western country. Third, it is the centre of a great colonial empire. These three circumstances combine to make its requirements and obligations quite unlike those of any other country (Japan is perhaps the most similar), and cause it to illustrate in an especially vivid way the salient features in the economics of plants.

If we think of Great Britain as it is to-day it is sometimes difficult to remember that it has not always been a great and thickly populated industrial and imperial country, and still more difficult to realise that the changes which have made it so have taken place comparatively recently and almost entirely in the last two hundred years.

At the beginning of the eighteenth century the population of the country was about 6½ millions and, to a great extent, was scattered over the countryside in small market towns and in villages. Only about a quarter was in the larger towns. The chief cities were London with 500,000 people; Bristol with 40,000; and Norwich, York, and Exeter. The wealthiest counties were in the midlands and south, and among the poorest in England were Yorkshire, Lancashire, Durham and Northumberland. Great Britain was, in short, a typical agricultural land providing the staple foods for its own population and exporting the surplus. Industries in the modern sense of the word were almost non-existent and, such as there were, were not organised on a factory system but were carried on in the workers' own homes. Much of the land was in the hands of small yeoman farmers; the immemorially old open-field method of farming was still widely employed; and the rotation of crops had not yet been introduced. Rye was the staple food cereal, and tea, coffee, cocoa and sugar were rather rare and expensive luxuries. The very indifferent and scanty roads were the only means of land transport.

Towards the middle of the century a change began to set in. Population increased slowly but steadily as it had been accustomed to do, and the enclosure of common-land on various grounds of expediency at the same time deprived many of the yeoman of the land from which they gained their living. There resulted from this and kindred causes a movement of people away from the rural areas to the towns, leaving more people to be fed and fewer people to feed them. This had a serious effect upon agriculture and by about 1770 the grain surplus had disappeared and it became necessary to import wheat and other cereals. Actually, in the last quarter of the century corn *imports* were four times as great as corn exports. In the first quarter of the century corn *exports* had been sixteen times as great as corn imports.

This movement towards the towns would probably in any case have ultimately caused considerable changes in national organisation, but it so happened that it was accompanied by other circumstances which had far more immediate and extensive results. Hitherto the iron industry of the country had been mainly centred in the forest areas of the south of England, where the wood fuel used for smelting the ore was abundant, but by the middle of the eighteenth century the supplies of timber here were seriously diminishing. Search was made for alternative fuels, and at the critical period the invention of the blast furnace made practicable the use of coal for the purpose. Almost simultaneously steam power also was introduced and in a very short time the industry had migrated to the coalfields and iron was being produced in unprecedented quantities.

With the cheap production of iron the stage was set for a whole sequence of far-reaching changes, to which as a whole the name of The Industrial Revolution is applied, changes which, commencing in the last quarter of the eighteenth century, converted the country, in the course of a few decades, from a rural agricultural community to an urban mechanical one. Steam and iron together made machinery, and with machinery all things were possible.

The whole revolution was rather like the firing of a gun. For countless centuries there had lain hidden in the coal seams of Great Britain almost incalculable wealth and power, but until the late eighteenth century no really practical method of exploiting it was known. Its only use was for domestic heating, and transport limitations prevented this from being very important. The discovery of steam and other contemporary advances forged a key which finally unlocked the whole resources of the coalfields and in so doing revolutionised the whole western world.

The coming of machinery brought with it the power to manufacture in quantity, and very soon Great Britain was supplying not only her own people but also much of the rest of the world with manufactured articles. By 1850 the country had earned the titles of the "Workshop of the World" and the "Mistress of the Seas", and these expressed in epigrammatic form the greatness of the changes which had taken place. The immediate result was enormous material wealth and a considerably wider dispersal of it. The middle class of society appeared as a new stratum between the aristocracy and the peasants and very quickly gained a great measure of power. The standard of living rose, the value of labour increased, and people all over the world clamoured for Britain's produce. We manufactured and the world was our customer.

But these changes, and other tendencies which we cannot discuss here, had another effect. Population, which had almost always been increasing slowly, suddenly began to rise by leaps and bounds, so that the figures increase from the $6\frac{1}{2}$ millions in 1700 to $8\frac{1}{2}$ in 1790, to 14 in 1820, to 21 in 1850, to 30 in 1880, to 40 in 1910 and to about 45 at the present time. By 1770 or so the figures had passed the point at which it was possible for the country to be self-supporting as regards its essential supplies, and ever since then the scales have been tilting more and more in the opposite direction. To-day it is said that Great Britain has to buy annually from other countries food to the value of nearly 400 millions sterling.

Owing to the great deposits of coal in the country and to the inventive genius of many of her countrymen, Great Britain started in the industrial race with great advantages, and for many years the demand for her goods was almost greater than the supplies available. While this happy condition of affairs prevailed the growth of population and trade seemed entirely and exclusively beneficial, since the one recruited the other, and the other could be expanded to keep pace with the one. It is only in the years since 1914 that the reverse side of the picture has revealed itself.

From a commercial point of view the Great War resolved itself to a great extent into a complicated series of intentional and accidental blockades and boycotts, the results of which were to dislocate almost all the normal systems of trade. Both old and new customers of the belligerent nations, and especially of Great Britain, could not get their orders fulfilled and were forced back upon their own resources. For their own sakes they were forced to manufacture for themselves the articles which they needed and which they had hitherto imported, so that to-day a great deal of Britain's overseas export trade has disappeared. The seriousness of this lies in the fact that trade so lost can hardly ever be regained. In pre-War days our overseas trade in manufactured goods flourished because we were able to supply countries with what they wanted much more cheaply than they could establish the industries and manufacture the articles for themselves. The sort of situation that was common is illustrated by cotton. Raw cotton was grown in India, bought and shipped to England, manufactured into cloth, bought again by India and re-shipped there once more. The War altered much of this. Customers were forced at whatever initial cost to become their own manufacturers, so that when peace came there was no necessity for them to renew their trade with Britain. From our point of view the remedy lies in the development of new industries which will be independent of the War's aftermath and which will reproduce the earlier conditions of prosperity, but this is very difficult. Unfortunately personnel and plant cannot be turned over from one direction to another without great inconvenience and disorganisation, and the present problem of unemployment is to a great extent a symptom of this and of the relatively unproductive period of transition.

The maintenance of the food and raw material supplies required by a population must always be the primary focus of activity of the people, and its maintenance by a complicated system of international trade is satisfactory so long as two conditions hold. There must be the means of production and ability to produce either natural or manufactured commodities, and there must be a sufficient and ready market for their consumption. In simpler phrase it needs two to trade, one to buy and one to sell. The country needing to import food does so by selling its manufactures and, with the proceeds of the transaction, buys what it requires. This method is sufficient so long as it functions, but its failure to do so is likely to have the most serious consequences. The submarine campaign of 1917 is an adequate illustration of what may happen to a densely peopled country when it does not function properly.

It is a characteristic of human nature that rewards seem more glittering than penalties or consequences seem threatening, and this was particularly true of the Industrial Revolution. Here was wealth almost for the asking, and if there were doubts and apprehensions they were quickly smothered under an avalanche of gold. Unheedful of the possible consequences the country sacrificed its material independence on the altar of immediate prosperity. The poet might well lament

> Ill fares the land to hastening ills a prey,
> Where wealth accumulates, and men decay;
> Princes and lords may flourish, or may fade,
> A breath can make them, as a breath hath made,
> But a bold peasantry, their country's pride,
> When once destroyed can never be supplied.

From a corn-exporting country, based on agriculture and commercially independent of the rest of the world, Britain became the greatest of industrial nations, with a huge population and with its economic fabric based on international overseas trade, a basis which has recently revealed its potential weaknesses only too plainly.

The degree of our dependence upon outside sources for the chief articles of vegetable foods can best be illustrated by a series of simple figures. Of wheat, which is still the staple food commodity, we grow at home about one-fifth of what we need, the rest has to be imported. Of barley we grow about half our requirements. In oats on the other hand we are more or less independent of imports and even more so is this the case with potatoes, of which the proportion imported is very small. In these two crops, oats and potatoes, we are more self-sufficient than in any others. In very many other items the proportions of home and imported supplies are about equal. In most temperate fruits like apples we are chiefly dependent on imports. The home sugar-beet industry is capable of supplying us with enough sugar to last about six weeks, that is to say about one-ninth of our annual needs.

Besides these a number of items now considered of importance in our diet come entirely from overseas, since they are the products of tropical plants that cannot be grown in this country. Such are tea, coffee, cocoa, spices, rice, tapioca, and fruits like the bananas and oranges. In vegetable raw materials the same is true, and of the four great industries—rubber, cotton, fibres and timber—only the last is at all appreciably supplied from home sources. Even in this one the home sources of supply are quite inadequate, and there is a great import trade in timber. In the other three the products are all derived from overseas, with the very minor exception of some of the flax. It is perfectly true that the Industrial Revolution can scarcely be blamed for the fact that the climate of the country is not tropical, but the connection between them is not so irrelevant as would at first sight appear. The importance of these tropical products in our economy is directly due to the indirect effects and changes in outlook consequent upon the Industrial Revolution.

It is now time to turn to another of the unique features of Great Britain—its great empire. The growth of this empire has had, as we shall see, a very great influence on the development of national economics. In 1700 the British Empire as we know it to-day was practically non-existent. There were settlements on the mainland of North America, especially on the east coast, and Newfoundland, despite its name, had been long a possession. We also owned the Bahamas, Jamaica and many smaller West Indian islands. In Africa we had no possessions and the continent was almost unexplored. Our Asiatic Empire had scarcely begun and Australia and New Zealand had not yet been discovered. To-day the Empire is world-wide, with an area 150 times, and a population 10 times, that of the mother country.

That the grand period of colonial expansion in the eighteenth and nineteenth centuries coincided with the Industrial Revolution was a circumstance of the first importance because at the critical time it tended to increase markets, to furnish certain commodities advantageously and to provide an outlet for emigration. Indeed it is questionable whether, had there been no Empire, Great Britain could have maintained her supremacy in industry for so long, especially in the later days of intense competition. Even now trade within the Empire is very much a family concern, and in the earlier days of closer co-operation this was still more true. Reciprocal trading agreements are possible in a way impracticable among independent nations, and the imperial bond has always been a great protection against the risk of concerted antagonism from competitive countries.

The actual part which the Empire plays in supplying the mother country with its necessities can also be illustrated shortly by some figures. Of the imported portions of our supplies in different commodities the Empire furnishes the following shares. About one-third of the wheat (Canada and Australia), a small part of the barley (Canada), about one-quarter of the oats (Canada), almost all the rye (Canada), about one-third of the rice (India), one-third of the coffee (Africa and India), most of the tea (India), most of the arrow-root and sago (West Indies and Malay), most of the cocoa (West Africa), a small proportion of the oranges (South Africa and Palestine), a small proportion of the bananas (West Indies), about one-third of the sugar (scattered), and nearly all the spices (especially British Asia). Of the important raw materials a great deal of the rubber comes from British Malaya, and much of the cotton and other fibres from various places in the Empire.

This is a very superficial sketch of the bearing of economic botany upon the welfare and actions of the inhabitants of one of the great European nations. What is true of Great Britain is true in substance, though perhaps not in degree, of every other nation with a similar level of civilisation and culture. In them all, and indeed in all human communities, the fundamental biological needs of the human body require that an adequate supply of food-stuffs shall be the fundamental basis of their economic organisations. Some achieve this by home agriculture, others partly by this and partly by international trade, others again almost exclusively by international trade. To the latter class Great Britain belongs.

The story of our own country is, as we have seen, bound up with the story of the great change from agriculture to industry. The Industrial Revolution has been too vast and too recent to be reviewed in proper perspective as yet, and any conclusions as to its net result must be somewhat prejudiced by personal opinions and traditions. Quite possibly it was inevitable, not only in Great Britain but also in the other countries which subsequently followed suit: perhaps it would have been modified if the future could have been foreseen sufficiently clearly. Circumstances to-day have certainly tended to shake many old beliefs and hopes. But whatever conclusions the individual reader may hold the Industrial Revolution undoubtedly did one thing. It set in motion a machinery of buying to sell and of selling to buy which very soon became, in fact, beyond the control of those who initiated it. It has remained beyond effective control ever since. It cannot be stopped intentionally without the risk of grave disaster, and for the same reason every precaution must be taken to prevent accidental interference with it. With these precautions mankind is at present chiefly occupied.

MAP 7

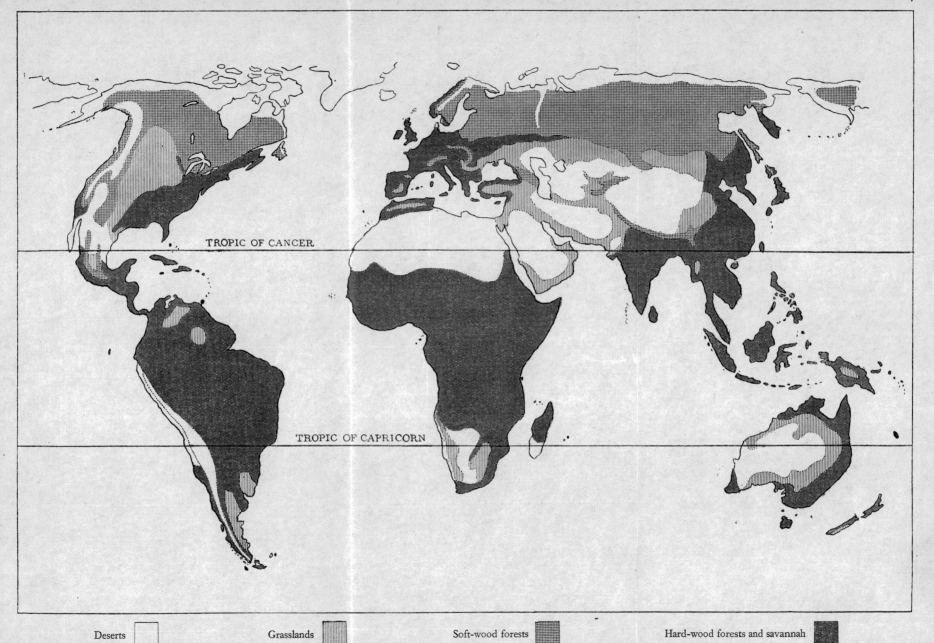

TROPIC OF CANCER

TROPIC OF CAPRICORN

Deserts   Grasslands   Soft-wood forests   Hard-wood forests and savannah

Map of the World showing the distribution of the three main types of natural vegetation, i.e. forests, grasslands, deserts.

SELECTED REFERENCE LIST

WILLIS, J. C. *Flowering-plants and Ferns*. Cambridge University Press.

BAILEY, L. H. *Hortus*. The Macmillan Company, New York.

PEATTIE, D. C. *Cargoes and Harvests*. Appleton.

BARRETT, O. W. *The Tropical Crops*. Macmillan.

WILCOX, E. V. *Tropical Agriculture*. Appleton.

THOMPSON, H. C. *Vegetable Crops*. McGraw-Hill Book Co.

NEWSHAM, J. C. *Crops and Tillage*. Methuen.

BRUTTINI, A. *Uses of Waste Materials*. King and Sons.

DE CANDOLLE, A. *Origin of Cultivated Plants*. Kegan Paul, Trench and Co.

MCINTOSH, T. P. *The Potato*. Oliver and Boyd.

ERNLE, LORD. *English Farming Past and Present*. Longmans, Green and Co.

LIPPINCOTT, I. *Economic Resources and Industries of the World*. Appleton.

HAYES, H. K. and GARBER, R. T. *Breeding Crop Plants*. McGraw-Hill Book Co.

BUTLER, H. *The United Kingdom*. Trade Promotion Series, 94, Washington.

MANTOUX, P. *The Industrial Revolution in the Eighteenth Century*. Jonathan Cape.

Pitman's Common Commodities and Industries Series. Pitman and Sons.

Annual Statements of the Trade of the United Kingdom. Stationery Office.

PHILIP and SHELDRAKE. *The Chambers of Commerce Atlas*.

RÜBEL, E. *Gesellschaften der Erde*. Huber (for the excellent and detailed vegetation map of the world by Dr Brockmann-Jerosch).

The British Pharmacopeia, 1932.

The British Pharmaceutical Codex, 1923.

APPENDIX

A combined list and index of the species and genera of seed-plants mentioned in the preceding chapters, arranged in systematic order, together with the common names applied to them or to their products.

ANGIOSPERMS
DICOTYLEDONS

PARIETALES (*cont.*)   PAGES
  Dipterocarpaceae (*cont.*)
    Dryobalanops aromaticus   Borneo camphor   134
    Shorea odorata   131
    S. robusta   sal tree   116
  Tamaricaceae
    Tamarix spp.   tamarisk   91, 159
  Cistaceae
    Cistus creticus   gum cistus   133
    C. ladaniferus   133
  Bixaceae
    Bixa Orellana   annatto   136
  Violaceae
    Viola spp.   violet   101, 105
  Flacourtiaceae
    Gynocardia odorata   98
    Hydnocarpus spp.   97
    Taraktogenos Kurzii   chaulmoogra oil   96
  Passifloraceae
    Passiflora edulis   passion fruit   80
    P. lancifolia   water lemon   80
    P. maliformis   sweet calabash   80
    P. quadrangularis   granadilla   80
  Caricaceae
    Carica Papaya   papaw   83

OPUNTIALES
  Cactaceae
    Nopalea coccinellifera   136
    Opuntia spp.   prickly pear   83

MYRTIFLORAE
  Thymelaeaceae
    Lagetta lintearia   lace bark   144
  Elaeagnaceae
    Hippophaë rhamnoides   sea buckthorn   159
  Lythraceae
    Lawsonia inermis   henna   135
    Physocalymma scaberrimum   tulip wood   118

MONOCOTYLEDONS

		PAGES
HELOBIAE		
Potamogetonaceae		
Zostera marina	eel grass	144
GLUMIFLORAE		
Gramineae		
Andropogon Nardus	oil	101
A. citratus	oil	101
Avena sativa	oats	62
Bromus Mango		65
Coix Lacryma-Jobi	Job's tears	65
Digitaria exilis		65
D. Iburua		65
Echinochloa frumentacea	cockspur millet	65
E. pyramidalis		65
E. stagnina		65
Eleusine coracana	ragi	65
Elymus arenarius	lyme grass	159
Eragrostis abyssinica	teff	65
Euchlaena mexicana	teosinte	64, 65
Hordeum vulgare	barley	62
Oryza sativa	rice	64, 100
Panicum miliaceum	broom-corn millet	65
P. maximum	Guinea grass	65
Paspalum scrobiculatum	Koda millet	65
Pennisetum typhoideum	pearl millet	65
Phragmites communis	reed	144
Psamma arenaria	marram	159
Saccharum officinarum	sugar cane	88
Secale cereale	rye	63
Setaria italica	Italian millet	65
Sorghum caffrorum	Kaffir corn	65
S. Durrha	durra	65
S. guineense	Guinea corn	65
S. vulgare	millet	65
Spartina Townsendii	cord grass	143
Stipa tenacissima	esparto grass	143
Triticum durum	wheat	61
T. polonicum	wheat	61

PRINCIPES (*cont.*)   PAGES
  Palmae (*cont.*)

Raphia Ruffia	raffia	143
Sabal Palmetto	palmetta	143
Sagus spp.	sago	91

SYNANTHAE
  Cyclanthaceae

Carludovica palmata	Panama hats	144

SPATHIFLORAE
  Araceae

Arum maculatum	cuckoo-pint	92
Monstera deliciosa	ceriman	83

FARINOSAE
  Bromeliaceae

Ananas sativus	pineapple	81
A. spp.		142
Tillandsia spp.		143

LILIIFLORAE
  Juncaceae

Juncus effusus	rush	143

  Liliaceae

Allium ascalonicum	shallots	73
A. Cepa	onion	73
A. fistulosum	chipple	73
A. Porrum	leek	73
A. sativum	garlic	73
A. Schoenoprasum	chives	73
Aloe spp.		151
Asparagus officinalis	asparagus	73
Dracaena cinnabari	dragon's blood	131
Colchicum officinale	colchicum	151
Phormium tenax	New Zealand flax	142
Sansevieria zeylanica	bowstring hemp	142
Scilla spp.	hyacinth	101
Tulipa Gesneriana	tulip	158
Urginea Scilla	squill	151

GYMNOSPERMS

INDEX

CAMBRIDGE : PRINTED BY W. LEWIS, M.A., AT THE UNIVERSITY PRESS